Practical
Pharmacoeconomics

How to design, perform and analyze outcomes research

LORNE E. BASSKIN, PHARM.D.

Advanstar Communications, Inc.

ii

Practical Pharmacoeconomics

Printed in the United States of America

10 9 8 7 6 5 4 3 2 1

ISBN 0-929870-46-8

Published by Advanstar Communications, Inc., 7500 Old Oak Blvd., Cleveland, Ohio 44130 USA.

Advanstar Communications is a U.S. business information company that publishes magazines and journals, produces expositions and conferences, and provides a wide range of marketing services.

Cover and interior design: Jon Dallman, Advanstar Communications, Duluth, Minnesota.

For additional copies of this book or for customized copies, please contact
        Lorne E. Basskin, Pharm.D.,
        Director of Continuing Education,
        Butler University College of Pharmacy and Health Sciences,
        4600 Sunset Avenue
        Indianapolis, IN 46208-3485
        FAX: 317-940-6172
        Phone: 317-940-8376
        Email: Basskin@Butler.edu

Each copy is $34.95 plus $4 shipping. Include $1.75 sales tax if order will be shipped to the state of Indiana. Quantity discounts available.

How to Obtain Continuing Education Credit

This book is designed to provide continuing education credit to pharmacists. Each chapter has been accredited for 1.5 contact hours (0.15 CEUs). The processing fee for each chapter is $7.

 Butler University College of Pharmacy and Health Sciences is approved by the American Council on Pharmacy Education as a provider of continuing pharmaceutical education. ACPE ID numbers for each of the chapters are available upon request.

For further information, please contact Dr. Lorne Basskin by phone, FAX, email or snail mail to obtain copies of the program evaluation forms and post continuing education answer sheets for the relevant chapters. Indicate the following:

1. Name
2. Mailing address
3. Phone number where you can be reached during the day
4. Email address
5. FAX number
6. Social Security number
7. The specific chapters for which you would like to obtain CEUs

After completing and submitting the tests and evaluation forms, accompanied by a check in the amount of $7 times the number of chapters being assessed, certificates of completion will be mailed to those who obtain a score of 70% or more on the post test. Those who fail to do so will be notified and an additional opportunity to increase their grade to 70% will be offered to them.

Send all requests for information to:

Lorne E. Basskin, Pharm.D.
Director of Continuing Education
Butler University College of Pharmacy and Health Sciences
4600 Sunset Avenue
Indianapolis, IN 46208-3485
FAX: 317-940-6172
Phone: 317-940-8376
Email: Basskin@Butler.edu

Foreword

I'm pleased to be able to offer this collection of modified versions of my first twenty columns, originally published in 1996 and 1997 in <u>Formulary</u> Magazine under the title "Practical Pharmacoeconomics".

The purpose of the column, and of this book, is to meet the needs of those who want to learn more about the practical aspects of pharmacoeconomics and outcomes research. There are other books and articles which discuss the theory of outcomes research and pharmacoeconomics in greater detail than I do in my column. However, the column was designed to respond to requests from health care practitioners who wanted (and needed) to know how to design, perform, analyze, interpret and apply original and/or published outcome research studies in their own setting.

I've chosen to publish this book in response to the many requests I have received for reprints of earlier columns. It's my hope that students, pharmacists, physicians, researchers and other healthcare professionals will be able to use the techniques I've described (and illustrated with examples) to meet the needs of information users and decision makers (patients, practitioners, and administrators) in their own institution.

A note of caution: Please don't use the actual results from the examples for decision making. When I was devising examples, or showing the results and conclusions from actual research, I tried to use realistic patient scenarios, dose regimens, costs of healthcare resources and measures of efficacy. However, since the goal of this book is help readers learn to use pharmacoeconomic techniques so that they may apply them in their own setting, except where otherwise indicated, the data shown is either hypothetical or was modified to better demonstrate the technique.

I hope you find this book useful and informative. As you read through each chapter, try to visualize how a problem in your institution is similar to one I've described in the examples. What outcomes would you have selected, and which costs of healthcare resources would be most relevant from your perspective?

I welcome your comments and suggestions for future columns. Write, phone or email me if the urge strikes you. Let me know if you agree or disagree with something I wrote. Let me hear how you are utilizing these techniques in your institution, or about problems you've encountered in study design, data collection or analysis.

The best part of publishing a book is the chance to thank those people who provided me with guidance and support. I want to express my appreciation and thanks to:

Dan James and Edward Wong, clinical pharmacists at Valley Medical Center, Renton, WA, who showed me that the only limits to a pharmacist directly affecting patient outcomes are one's skill, desire, and ability to collaborate and communicate with other healthcare professionals,

My academic mentors over the years, Richard Abood, Kathy Knapp and Robert Supernaw from the University of the Pacific, Robert Sandmann, Sharon Hammerich and Bruce Clayton from Butler University, and Nicholas

Popovich of Purdue University. They have helped me improve my teaching and writing skills, are vocal supporters of innovative and relevant teaching methodologies, and provided me with encouragement and support to pursue my personal and professional goals,

My students, who have always been the first to let me know if my efforts at introducing a new concept or employing a new teaching methodology were a success or a disaster,

Formulary's editor, Karen Sprague, for her assistance in editing my columns, enabling readers to more easily comprehend both principles and examples,

My children, Ian, Katie, Allison and Aaron, and my loving spouse and best friend Judi, for their unconditional support and patience in allowing me the opportunity to pursue my dreams and goals, and

My loyal readers, who have kindly provided me with feedback and ideas for columns. May all your research be productive and your analyses informative and may your decision makers never suffer from lack of useful information.

Lorne E. Basskin, Pharm.D.
Indianapolis, IN
January 15, 1998

Table of Contents

Table of Contents

What is the Difference between Pharmacoeconomics and Outcomes Research?

Learning Objectives:

After reading this chapter, one should be able to:

1. Explain the differences and interrelationship between pharmacoeconomics and outcomes research.

2. Explain the role of pharmacoeconomics when selecting from among alternative therapies or clinical services.

3. List three reasons why pharmacoeconomics and outcomes research is of interest to practioners and decision-makers.

The purpose of this book is to help you learn how to design and perform outcomes research, and learn to apply pharmacoeconomic techniques. Perhaps you are reading it because you want, or were asked by someone else, to determine which therapy, clinical service, medical device or surgical procedure was most cost-effective. However, perhaps you are skeptical about the whole process of choosing cost-effective therapies and haven't yet decided if this book is for you. Let's explore that concept further.

Why should you care about choosing the most cost-effective medications for an entire sub-population of patients? After all, most healthcare professionals were trained with the philosophy that the each patient is unique and needs individualized therapy. In addition, many people think it is unethical to save costs by selecting therapy which offers less than the maximum effectiveness available.

When resources were unlimited, there were few believers in the concept that health care costs had to be reduced. However, in the 1980's, when the amount spent on health care in the United States began to increase by about $30-$50 billion per year, those who paid for the care of patients started looking for ways to decrease the amount spent for health care. Methods adopted, many of which are still in existence, included the use of generic drugs, formulary control and therapeutic substitution of drugs, fixed fees for services (regardless of the actual costs of care), shortened length-of-stay, and the use of less expensive procedures and medications.

Healthcare institutions quickly realized that for them to survive the downward pressure on revenue and increased pressure on costs, they would need to decrease costs of care. After some experimentation, a discipline of health economics surfaced in which models were developed to assist decision makers in this process of selecting drugs and therapies. The goal was to find treatments which enabled the goals of therapy to be met at the lowest possible cost. Two fundamental principles emerged.

The first principle was the recognition that patients could be categorized by, and grouped into, similar populations. While individual therapy might need to be monitored and adjusted, initial or empiric therapy could be planned and ordered on a population basis. This allowed for standardized care plans and widespread use of cost-minimization techniques. The second principle was that it would not be financially possible for every patient to receive therapy which had the maximum effectiveness. Sacrifices in efficacy would have to be made in order to avoid harsher rationing, and ultimately, refusal of care.

The process by which different therapies or drug regimens are evaluated in order to measure the extent to which a goal of therapy, or desirable outcome can be reached, is known as outcomes research. Outcomes which have been identified in the literature as relevant for patients include economic, clinical, and humanistic outcomes. Kozma and Reeder summarized this concept as the ECHO model in an article that is well worth reading.[1]

Examples of outcomes research methodology include retrospective chart review, prospective clinical trials, and observational studies. In addition to actually gathering data about patients, an alternative method is the use of computer software "models", in which cost and efficacy data is culled from published literature and cost-effectiveness is determined based on expected costs and efficacy. In some models, the researcher combines published data with that of a specific institution. Refer to Appendix III at the back of this book for a further discussion and comparison of these two techniques.

Pharmacoeconomics, a division of health care economics, is a tool, not a solution, designed to provide users and decision makers with information about the cost-effectiveness of different pharmacotherapies. It is used in combination with outcomes research, as an analytic tool in which the results of research are manipulated and modified using different mathematical techniques. The goal of pharmacoeconomics is to recommend the most cost-effective agent at achieving a designated outcome in a specific population. However, when one agent is both more expensive and more effective, it provides information about the incremental or marginal cost per outcome to be obtained (cost per extra life saved).

Finally, we need a working definition of the term "cost-effective"; not only to ensure consistency, but because you'll often be asked to explain the meaning of pharmacoeconomics to decision makers in your organization. I like to describe the cost-effective alternative as the one which provides the desired level of efficacy, at achieving an outcome, for the lowest possible cost.

So much for an overview of the topic. You will find specific examples of both pharmacoeconomic techniques and outcomes research methodology in the chapters ahead. In the meantime, I've summarized ten important points with which you should become familiar and will help you as you read each of the chapters.

1. The collection of techniques is called "pharmacoeconomics", because it centers around selection of cost-effective pharmacotherapy. However,

the same techniques can be applied when evaluating surgical procedures, medical devices or clinical services.

2. Evaluating alternative drug therapies doesn't mean that the costs are limited to those of the drugs alone. Generally, one needs to consider the effects of alternatives on all health care costs.

3. Since the purpose of research is to study a sample of patients, and apply the results to a larger population, a basic understanding of statistics is essential when either reading the analyses of other or performing analysis of your own research. A <u>New England Journal of Medicine</u> study found that you could understand the statistical analysis in 70% of the articles published in that magazine with an understanding of just some basic statistical tests. As a start, I suggest you read the primer on statistics in Appendix I at the back of this book.

4. Approach every published study, clinical or pharmacoeconomic, with a healthy degree of skepticism. Before using the results of the study in your own decision making process, ask yourself if assumptions are reasonable, if the design is valid, if the costs are similar to your own, and if the population is typical of yours.

5. Every drug, service or procedure needs to have a goal or outcome you want to achieve. Try to choose outcomes that are from SMART; Sustainable, Measurable, Attainable, Relevant and Timely.

6. A cost-effective drug, service or procedure must first be effective before its costs are considered. Therefore, you need to have a good knowledge about the therapeutic issues of a disease state or drug before you start to consider the costs of drugs and related care.

7. The use of a formulary as a means on controlling inappropriate drug use is a first step towards solving that problem. However, it is just as important that the drugs available are used appropriately, and that's where disease state management, drug use guidelines and clinical pathways become important tools. Instead of choosing a drug for all purposes, consider selecting drugs suitable for a specific population, for a specific disease state, and directed towards accomplishing a specific goal or desired outcome.

8. While pharmacists are often entrusted with the job of recommending and purchasing drugs for the institution, it's a mistake to think of the pharmacy department (and the cost of drugs alone) as the most relevant or only perspective. In some cases, a more cost-effective therapy may involve more expensive drugs, but a lower <u>total</u> cost of care.

9. Rarely do the people doing the research and analysis know all of the facts about the institution's available resources, contractual commitments and pre-determined standards of care. Therefore, the role of pharmacoeconomists and researchers is not to make a decision, but to provide decision-makers with relevant information about both cost and efficacy so that they may select from among alternative therapies. For example, suppose a cost-effectiveness analysis calculated the cost per year of life saved with Drug A as less than that of a more expensive but more effective Drug B. It is the job of the decision makers, and not the re-

searcher or analyst, to select Drug A or B based on the answers to (at least) three important questions:

A. If Drug A is chosen because it is more effective, is the extra cost of Drug A both a *reasonable* and *affordable* price to pay to prolong life of a patient by one more year?

B. If less expensive but less effective Drug B is chosen, have any legal, contractual or ethical rules been violated?

C. If less expensive Drug B is chosen, will it provide an acceptably effective level and quality of patient care?

Answering these questions requires not only a consideration of the resources required (both per patient and for the entire institution), but also a knowledge of

- resources available to the institution,
- any contractual commitments of the responsible institution with its members or other persons paying for healthcare,
- the acceptable standards of care of the community and the organization, and
- the legal consequences, and impact on the institution's reputation and credibility, of selecting one standard of care over another.

REFERENCES

1. Kozma CM, Reeder CE, Schultz RM. "Economic, clinical, and humanistic outcomes: a planning model for pharmacoeconomic research." Clin Ther 1993; Nov;15(6):1121-1132.

Using cost-minimization analysis to collect and analyze costs associated with adverse drug events

Learning Objectives:

After reading this chapter, one should be able to:

1. Distinguish between different types of costs and explain the importance of marginal costs in a pharmacoeconomic analysis.

2. List each of the healthcare resources used by a patient if an adverse drug event were to occur.

3. Utilize cost-minimization analysis to determine the cost of different categories of ADEs, and to select those categories which merit interventions.

One task of P & T Committees at most hospitals and managed care organizations is to review ADE or ADR reports. After converting, sorting, and summarizing data from patient charts, ADE reports are usually organized by offending drug or by prescribing physician, and then categorized as mild, moderate, or severe. The different methods of uncovering concurrent and retrospective ADEs, including the use of ICD-9 codes, have been written about previously[1-3] and will not be discussed here. What will be discussed is what ADE-related cost information to collect once ADEs have been identified and how to analyze the data to determine which ADEs are associated with the highest costs.

WHAT ADE-ASSOCIATED COSTS SHOULD BE COLLECTED?

Before beginning the pharmacoeconomic analysis of ADEs, decide on the goal of the analysis. One reasonable goal might be to reduce the number of ADEs suspected to be avoidable, thereby reducing ADE-associated costs.

After uncovering the number and types of ADEs, the next step is to identify and accumulate the costs. The first step in this process is to determine perspective. Whose costs are to be minimized—the patient's, the third party payer's, or the institution's? Whatever perspective is selected, make sure that the cost items and the amounts selected are relevant to the perspective chosen.

From the perspective of a hospital, there are a number of obvious ADE-related costs that make sense to collect (see Exhibit 1). The goal is to identify the "marginal cost" of an ADE: the extra future cost associated with the occurrence of one more or one less ADE. Marginal costs are not the same as historic costs; the latter contains elements of both past inefficiencies and fixed costs. In an ADE analysis, I try to estimate marginal costs in the future by first identifying, and then estimating, direct and indirect costs of the past that var-

EXHIBIT 1

ADE-associated costs to collect

Keep in mind that collection of the following costs must be relevant to the perspective chosen—either the patient, third party payer, or institution.

Marginal costs: These are the predicted *future* direct and indirect costs that will vary directly with the occurrence or avoidance of ADEs. They are estimated by looking at variable costs of the past.

Variable costs. These are the *historic* costs that increased as the number of patients admitted for ADEs in the institution increased. They include relevant indirect costs, direct patient care costs, and direct drug costs. They are used as the basis for predicting marginal costs, and will equal marginal costs if no changes in prices, wages, efficiency, or productivity are expected in the future.

Fixed costs. These are costs that are not variable; i.e., they do not change with the number of patients admitted for ADEs.

Indirect costs. These are costs that are necessary for the institution to function, but are not directly related to patient care. They could be fixed (the cost of the building, accounting staff) or vary with patient census (staff pharmacists' wages, laundry, maintenance).

Direct drug costs. These costs are the institution's actual acquisition costs of the drug, labor, and materials necessary to prepare, distribute, and administer the drugs and monitor their effects. They include the cost of time spent by pharmacists, technicians, and nurses in preparing and administering the drugs, as well as the cost of any pumps, solutions, or syringes needed.

Other ADE-related costs to *consider* collecting

Whether or not to calculate the following costs or adjustments to cost depends on the perspective chosen and practice setting.

■ Revenue gained from billing for the ADE.

■ Physician costs for treating the ADE.

■ Patient's intangible costs for pain and suffering, inconvenience, and lost time from work.

ied with the occurrence of ADEs. Fixed costs and variable costs that are unrelated to ADEs are excluded from the analysis.

Variable costs (as opposed to fixed costs) are those that are expected to increase as a result of the ADE or decrease if the ADE is avoided. The costs could be either indirect (administration, overhead) or directly related to patient care. Indirect patient care costs are a relevant variable cost that should be collected if they change as a result of the ADE occurring or being prevented. For example, the costs of opening a closed floor or nursing unit are relevant variable costs to consider if such openings occur as a result of ADEs.

Another variable cost to collect is direct drug costs. More specifically, direct drug costs should include the acquisition cost of the drug plus the cost of preparation, distribution, administration, and monitoring. If the ADE was attributable to an incorrect drug regimen and the drug costs are thought to be significant, consider adding the cost of the proper drug that should have been given, and subtracting the costs of the drugs that were given incorrectly.

How should the direct daily costs of taking care of a patient (costs, not patient charges) be calculated into the ADE cost equation? Some advocate that 100% of the institution's daily direct and indirect costs should be included in the marginal cost calculations since all of the institution's costs will eventually increase as the number of patients admitted for ADE-related events increases. On the other hand, depending on the practice setting, many costs of care are fixed because the patient care costs would not decrease even if the number of ADEs were reduced. In the latter case, consider identifying specific non-drug costs associated with a patient stay or an ER visit.

Personally, I prefer to focus on costs that change over the short term. I usually exclude the costs of major expansions or closing of wings of the facility or nursing units, the cost of buying new equipment, and the cost of administrative overhead because they are usually fixed costs and don't vary as a result of ADE occurrence or avoidance.

While some might argue that the operating costs for nurses, lights, and laundry are required every day and therefore are fixed costs, fewer patients admitted for ADEs decreases the institution's expected patient census, a number upon which many staffing and purchasing decisions are made and are better described as variable costs. This may not be true in your practice setting. You can also choose to treat a percentage of a certain cost as variable (i.e.—treat 50% of nursing salaries as variable if the nursing workload could increase somewhat before additional nursing labor is required).

Before beginning to collect data, you should have identified those direct and indirect cost components (also called health care resources) that you believe will vary in the future with the number of ADEs. In this column, I used length of stay or emergency room visit plus the direct costs of extra lab tests, monitoring, and drugs administered *per individual* ADE as the components of ADE-related marginal cost.

Due to all the cost variables to consider, develop a data input sheet to sort and categorize each ADE. Collect such information as the patient's name, age, and sex; name of the prescribing physician; drugs implicated; organ system affected; drug(s) used to treat the ADE; lab and other tests ordered; the reason for the avoidable ADE (compliance problem, inappropriate drug/regimen, drug interaction); and the number of extra day(s) of hospital stay and/or the occurrence of an emergency room (ER) visit.

Of all the ADE-associated costs to consider, perhaps the easiest way to begin the collection process is to start with resources whose costs remain unchanged for each ADE, such as an ER admission or extra day(s) of stay. Quite often, the institution knows its patient charge for these services, but is un-

TABLE 1 — DIFFERENT METHODS OF SORTING AND SUMMARIZING ADE OCCURRENCES AND COSTS

Summary of avoidable ADEs for Hospital for Jan 1 to March 31, 1997

	(A) No. of ADEs	(B) ER visits	(C) Extra days of stay	(D) Drug costs	(E) Monitoring & lab costs	(F) Total costs*	(G) Average cost/ADE†
By drug or drug class							
Digoxin	7	7	16	$2,100	$650	$19,175	$2,739
Theophylline	12	2	19	750	250	19,400	1,617
Beta blockers	14	2	8	560	100	8,610	615
Diuretics	18	8	8	950	300	10,250	569
All other	7	1	9	540	50	9,315	1,331
Total	58	20	60	$4,900	$1,350	$66,750	$1,151
By prescribing physician							
Dr. Smith	11	11	20	$2,750	$420	$24,095	$2,190
Dr. Jones	25	0	18	1,500	100	18,700	748
Dr. Walleye	12	6	18	520	730	19,400	1,617
All other	10	3	4	130	100	4,555	456
Total	58	20	60	$4,900	$1,350	$66,750	$1,151
By cause of avoidable ADE							
Noncompliance	19	13	30	$2,500	$350	$33,625	$1,770
Drug interaction	19	6	17	1,400	700	19,300	1,016
Incorrect drug/regimen	20	1	13	1,000	300	13,825	691
Total	58	20	60	$4,900	$1,350	$66,750	$1,151
By organ system							
Cardiovascular	20	15	25	$3,100	$1,000	$30,475	$1,524
GI	20	4	16	800	120	16,820	841
Renal	7	1	16	620	150	16,145	2,306
All other	11	0	3	380	80	3,310	301
Total	58	20	60	$4,900	$1,350	$66,750	$1,151

*Cost of ER visit is $175/admission and cost of hospital stay is $950/day. Total costs are calculated as: (column B x $175) + (column C x $950) + column D + column E.

† Average cost per ADE is calculated as total cost per line entry divided by the number of ADEs per line entry (i.e., column F divided by column A).

Formulary/Source: L. Basskin, PharmD

aware of its own actual (or allocated) costs. In that case, you can estimate these costs by multiplying your charges by a factor of between 0.6 and 0.9—which is probably the hospital's ratio of all costs: all charges.

While the drug, lab, and monitoring charges can be calculated manually for each patient, I suggest a predetermined amount (an average cost) for every lab test or antidote used can be assigned. In the latter case, just keep track of and add up the number of antidotes used or number of lab tests performed for each ADE, and multiply the total resources used times the average cost per resource.

"GREY AREA" COSTS

Some costs fall into the "grey area" in terms of deciding if they should be considered in ADE cost calculations. Most of these costs depend on the perspective of the user within the institution or on the type of practice setting.

For instance, should one reduce the costs of the ADEs by the amount gained from billing for the ADE? Generally, if patients are seen for a reason other than the ADE and are covered by Medicare or similar type plans, only one DRG is often allowed for the admission. Therefore, the costs of most ADEs are often not recoverable from third party payers. Meet with your billing department to find out the circumstances at your institution. Net costs (i.e., costs incurred less those recovered from billings) instead of total costs could be used in the analysis, if they are more relevant to the user of this information within the institution.

Should physician costs for treating the ADE be factored in? Consider adding in such costs if looking at the cost of ADEs from the perspective of the patient or if in a managed care setting; however, do not add costs if the perspective is that of a hospital, since they generally do not pay physician costs for treating an ADE.

What about intangible costs, such as patients' pain and suffering, inconvenience, and lost time from work? If analyzing the ADE from the patient's perspective, these items will have to be identified and costs assigned. From the institution's perspective, the only costs to be considered from these items (excluding any lawsuit award for pain and suffering) is the possible loss of future business from that customer, but this is extremely difficult to measure.

TARGETING HIGH-COST ADEs

Simply knowing the quantity of ADEs and some associated costs doesn't reveal which ADEs cost the institution the most money in total and per event—i.e., the ADEs that should be targeted to generate the largest financial return on the investment.

It should be kept in mind that although it is important to analyze severe ADEs—as they often indicate the need for immediate intervention, education, and in some cases, disciplinary action[4]—mild and moderate ADEs must be included in an economic analysis, as these ADEs can be associated with higher overall costs because they occur more frequently.

To visualize this concept, look at table 1. This table shows a sample summary spreadsheet of ADE-associated costs collected over a 3-month period at a fictitious hospital. Cost calculations are sorted, in this example, into four categories—drug or drug class, prescribing physician, cause of avoidable ADE, and organ system involved. After identifying the top three or four sources of ADEs in each category, the remainder were group under the "other" heading. For each category, the total number and cost of avoidable ADEs is now known.

By looking at only the number of ADEs in the table, one might draw the wrong conclusion as to what are the most expensive ADEs and which prescriber is associated with the highest ADE-related costs. For example, when sorted by drug or drug class, diuretics have the highest number of ADEs, but are associated with the lowest average cost at $569 per ADE. Digoxin, however, with the lowest number of ADEs of those listed separately, is associated with the highest average ADE cost at $2,739 per ADE, and its total costs are almost as high as the ADE costs attributed to theophylline.

When analyzing the result according to prescriber, even though Dr. Jones' patients experienced the most ADEs—almost half the total number of ADEs in this example—because his average ADE cost is $748, his total ADE cost is only third highest among physicians. Dr. Smith's patients, who experienced only 11 ADEs, were the biggest source of ADE costs because each of his patients' ADEs resulted in an ER visit and a hospital stay of almost 2 days.

When looking at the cause of the avoidable ADEs, each of the three reasons listed accounted for an equal number of ADEs. However, the costs differed significantly. The ADE costs attributed to noncompliance amounted to $33,625, which is almost three times more than ADE costs attributed to incorrect drug/regimens.

Similarly, when analyzing the results by organ system, renal ADEs appear to be the least problematic, since they accounted for only 7 of the 58 ADEs. However, at an average cost of $2,306, they are the most expensive ADE per event. An equal number of cardiovascular and GI-associated ADEs occurred. However, the cost of cardiovascular-associated ADEs, at $30,475, was almost twice the amount of GI-associated ADEs.

Thus, knowing just the quantity of ADEs, even when sorted by multiple categories, doesn't reveal which ADEs cost the institution the most money in total and per event. When implementing an ADE reducing strategy, one needs to know specifically where to intervene to save the most money.

In this chapter, discussion has centered on calculating costs associated with ADEs—both according to total number and by specific subgroups. The next chapter will discuss how to determine the costs of interventions that reduce the number of avoidable ADEs, how to estimate the likely success rate of an intervention, and how to select interventions that will result in the greatest net savings (costs of ADEs avoided less costs of the intervention) to the institution from avoiding ADEs.

REFERENCES

1. Leape LL, Bates DW, et al. "Systems analysis of adverse drug events." JAMA 1995;274:35-43.
2. Orsini MJ, Orsini Funk PA, Thorn DB, et al. "An ADR surveillance program: Increasing quality, number of incidence reports." Formulary 1995;30:454-61.
3. Saltiel E, Johnson E, Shane R. "A team approach to adverse drug reaction surveillance: Success at a tertiary care hospital." Hosp Formul 1995;30:226-32.
4. Hartwig SC, Siegel J, Schneider PJ. "Preventability and severity assessment in reporting adverse drug reactions." Am J Hosp Pharm 1992;49:2229-32.

Using cost-benefit analysis to select from alternative interventions designed to prevent the occurrence of adverse drug events

Learning Objectives:

After reading this chapter, one should be able to:

1. Interpret and explain the results of a cost-benefit analysis by analyzing total benefits, net benefits, benefit/cost ratio and return on investment.

2. Determine the costs, and healthcare costs saved, associated with different clinical interventions.

3. Using cost-benefit analysis, evaluate alternative interventions designed to avoid or decrease the incidence and costs associated with adverse drug events.

The last chapter examined how to calculate and analyze the costs associated with adverse drug events (ADEs) and how to sort information to identify which ADEs cost the facility—in this example, a hospital—the most money. This chapter describes how to apply cost-benefit analysis to different scenarios involving avoidable ADEs and potential interventions. The goal of using this pharmacoeconomic tool is to help select, from your perspective, the most appropriate and beneficial ADE to target.

Before discussing how to apply cost-benefit analysis to adverse drug events (ADEs) and possible interventions, some general background information on cost-benefit analysis, other cost-related terms, and sensitivity analysis should be presented.

Cost-benefit analysis (CBA) is a useful technique for evaluating alternatives with different outcomes, all of which are expressed in dollars (i.e., as opposed to natural units such as blood pressure, lives saved). Under CBA, both costs and benefits are measured and converted into dollars.

Besides costs and benefits, two other cost-related calculations can be made. The first is the benefit/cost ratio, which is equal to the total benefits divided by the cost. A ratio higher than 1.0 means that each dollar invested produces more than one dollar of benefits. The other number to calculate is the return on investment (ROI). This is equal to the net benefits divided by costs. The ROI represents that rate of return the institution earns on its investment in the project. As long as benefits are greater than costs, use of ROI or benefit/cost ratio results in equivalent ranking of alternatives. Both mea-

TABLE 1   COST-BENEFIT ANALYSIS OF HYPOTHETICAL PHARMACY PROJECTS

Alternative	Costs	Benefits	Net benefits*	Return on investment†	Benefit/ cost ratio‡
A	$50,000	$55,000	$5,000	10%	1.1
B	2,000	4,000	2,000	100%	2.0
C	200,000	212,000	12,000	6%	1.06
D	100,000	105,000	5,000	5%	1.05

* Net benefits equals benefits minus costs
† Return on investment equals net benefits divided by costs times 100%
‡ Benefit/cost ratio equals benefits divided by costs

Formulary/Source: L. Basskin, PharmD

sures are shown in the examples used in this article.

When evaluating alternatives using CBA, one should generally select the option with the highest net benefit. However, if more than one alternative has the same net benefits, then the alternative with the highest ROI or benefit/cost ratio should be selected.

CHOICE OF 'BEST' ALTERNATIVE DEPENDS ON PERSPECTIVE

To review the principles of CBA, examine table 1. Four pharmacy projects are under consideration. Costs, benefits, and other cost-related calculations for these projects are all shown. Which project should be selected? The answer depends on your perspective within your practice setting.

If your perspective is that of a manager of the entire institution, or if you are concerned with the total hospital budget, choice C should be selected. In this scenario, the net benefits to the hospital are the highest, and the particular department that spends the money versus obtains the benefits isn't an issue. This choice assumes, of course, that the hospital has sufficient funds to afford choice C.

If the perspective is that of the department director, whose budget will bear the project costs, the choice might differ. Alternative B generates the lowest net benefits, but has the highest ROI and requires spending the least amount of money. To the department director, this choice represents the most efficient use of funds. While choice B is probably not the best solution for the institution as a whole, selection of this alternative typically occurs when one department is asked to recommend an alternative for which they are responsible for costs but don't receive any of the benefits.

If the perspective is that of the accounting or finance department, the choice of alternative differs again. Although this group also wants to maximize net benefits, they may be concerned about the $200,000 required to implement choice C. Selection of such an alternative might require either borrowing money or reallocating dollars from another project that also promises benefits to the institution.

The ROI allows comparison of this project to other unrelated projects by using a common standard of measurement. For instance, even though the net benefits of choice A are lower than choice C ($5,000 vs $12,000), the finance department might recommend choice A if the hospital's cost of borrowing money is more than 6% (ie, higher than the ROI of choice C).

Finally, it is important to note that both the ROI and benefit/cost ratio can be used in tandem. If two projects each produce the same net benefits, choose the project with the highest ROI or benefit/cost ratio, as it means less dollars will be required to earn the same benefits. For instance, although choice A and D offer the same net benefits, choice A has a higher ROI and benefit/cost ratio, making it the more preferable choice.

In summary, the primary concern for the entire institution should be selecting alternatives with the highest net benefits, while keeping an eye on the ROI to ensure the rate of return meets a certain minimum.

What if the projected net benefits turn out to be much lower than expected because costs are higher or benefits are lower than expected? (The converse could also occur.) When conducting pharmacoeconomic analyses, one must take into account the effects of uncertainty by performing a *sensitivity analysis*. Using this technique, the range of best to worst possible outcomes can be seen for each alternative before a choice is made. For example, if two solutions to a problem are available, and both have an average net benefit of $100 and an ROI of 10%, it is impossible to know which solution is best to select. However, assume that the possible net benefits range from $90 to $110 for choice A, and from $0 to $200 for choice B. A conservative approach would be to choose option A, since the 'downside' benefit is only $10 less than the average net benefit. Risk takers, on the other hand, would select option B, enticed by the larger possible payoff.

APPLYING COST-BENEFIT ANALYSIS TO ADEs

Now let's use the CBA technique to solve the problem of which ADEs to target and which methods of intervention to select. A six-step process is involved. The steps are to:

1. Identify the perspective.
2. Identify the outcome or goal, and alternative outcomes.
3. Estimate the dollar benefits for each alternative.
4. Identify and estimate the relevant costs of each alternative from the same perspective as the benefits.
5. Calculate the net benefits and return on investment (or benefit/ cost ratio) for each alternative. Take into account uncertainty by performing sensitivity analysis on the costs and benefits if appropriate.
6. Select the interventions to be implemented.

In the example that follows, the perspective of the analysis will be that of the hospital. The goal is to reduce the cost of ADEs. The alternatives are the three most costly categories of avoidable ADEs identified in the previous chapter: ADEs associated with Dr Smith's patients, digoxin-related ADEs, and ADEs associated with noncompliance.

The benefits are defined as the reduction in the associated ADE costs. It is calculated as the expected ADE costs without any intervention multiplied by

TABLE 2	**FUTURE COSTS ASSOCIATED WITH THREE HYPOTHETICAL CATEGORIES OF AVOIDABLE ADEs**			
ADE type	No. of patients expected next year with potential for this type of ADE*	Historic average cost per ADE (at this institution)	Historic rate of ADE (occurrence at this institution)	Expected ADE costs for next year†
Dr Smith	2,500	$1,600	2.25%	$ 90,000
Digoxin	1,200	2,000	10%	240,000
Noncompliance	3,000	1,000	2.67%	80,000

* Based on historic data adjusted for next year's census
† Obtained by multiplying the three preceding columns together, per line entry

*Formulary/*Source: L. Basskin, PharmD

the expected percentage decrease in ADEs as a result of the intervention (e.g., expected associated ADE costs of $100,000 decreased by 20% results in a benefit of $20,000).

The ADE summary chart in the last chapter represented *historic* ADE costs. However, more important are *future* ADE costs. For each of the three alternatives under consideration, next year's ADE costs can be estimated by multiplying last year's rate of ADE occurrence times last year's average cost per ADE times the number of patients expected in the institution this next year with potential for this ADE type (table 2).

When estimating the costs of the interventions, use marginal costs, defined as those that will vary in the future as a result of the intervention (see Chapter 2 for a more complete explanation). If you can accomplish the intervention without increasing costs, say by using existing staff, then the marginal costs of those activities are much less than if you had to hire new staff to do the same activity. I calculate the marginal cost of interventions based on the hourly salary of the people who will perform the intervention.

One important step of CBA requires an estimate of the success of an intervention. Where an alternative therapy or intervention has been studied previously and published, it is possible to obtain probable success rates. Unfortunately, very few studies have been published regarding the success of interventions in reducing or eliminating ADEs. In the absence of published examples, use your own best judgment in estimating your success rates. Incorporate a broad range and perform sensitivity analysis.

In the examples that follow, an intervention strategy for each of the three ADE categories has been selected. Following the brief explanation of the tabulation of intervention costs per the ADE examples discussed, cost-benefit analysis techniques and sensitivity analysis will be applied to show how these techniques can aid in the selection of the most appropriate ADE category in which to intervene. For illustrative purposes, I've assumed that budgetary constraints limit the ability to intervene in all cases, and that only one of the three alternatives to reducing ADEs and their associated costs will be selected. Another approach could be to evaluate three alternative interventions (e.g.,

TABLE 3 **ANALYSIS OF SELECTED ADE CATEGORIES USING COST-BENEFIT ANALYSIS**

	Low costs High benefits	High costs High benefits	Low costs Low benefits	High costs Low benefits	Average
Dr Smith's ADEs					
Total expected cost of ADEs attributable to Dr Smith's patients	$90,000	$90,000	$90,000	$90,000	$90,000
Success rate	30%	30%	20%	20%	25%
Benefits	$27,000	$27,000	$18,000	$18,000	$22,500
Less cost of intervention (physician education)	$17,500	$18,500	$17,500	$18,500	$18,000
Net benefits	$9,500	$8,500	$1,500	($500)	$4,500
Benefit/cost ratio	1.5	1.5	1.0	1.0	1.3
Return on investment	54%	46%	3%	−3%	25%
Digoxin-related ADEs					
Total expected cost of ADEs attributable to digoxin	$240,000	$240,000	$240,000	$240,000	$240,000
Success rate	90%	90%	65%	65%	78%
Benefits	$216,000	$216,000	$156,000	$156,000	$186,000
Less cost of intervention (pharmacist intervention)	$150,000	$190,000	$150,000	$190,000	$170,000
Net benefits	$66,000	$26,000	$6,000	($34,000)	$16,000
Benefit/cost ratio	1.4	1.1	1.0	0.8	1.1
Return on investment	44%	14%	4%	−18%	9%
Noncompliance ADEs					
Total expected cost of ADEs attributable to noncompliance	$80,000	$80,000	$80,000	$80,000	$80,000
Success rate	50%	50%	30%	30%	40%
Benefits	$40,000	$40,000	$24,000	$24,000	$32,000
Less cost of intervention (patient counselling)	$18,000	$24,000	$18,000	$24,000	$21,000
Net benefits	$22,000	$16,000	$6,000	0	$11,000
Benefit/cost ratio	2.2	1.7	1.3	1.0	1.5
Return on investment	122%	67%	33%	0%	52%

Formulary/Source: L. Basskin, PharmD

face-to-face patient education, written patient information, telephone patient follow-up) per one ADE category.

For ADEs associated with Dr Smith's patients, I've selected physician education as the corrective intervention strategy. I estimate that a one time cost of $12,500 will be required for production and presentation of an ADE avoidance seminar and newsletter, plus an average of $10 to $12 per intervention (the cost of a 15 to 20 minute telephone call and corrective action). I expect that Dr. Smith will write orders for 2,500 patients, and I'm going to call him on approximately 20% of these orders. Therefore, intervention costs will range from $17,500 to $18,500 (i.e., $12,500 + [2,500 x 20% x {$10 or $12}]). I will assume that my interventional efforts will result in at least a 20% decrease in ADEs (based on that many direct interventions), but perhaps as much as 30% if education is even more successful.

For digoxin-related ADEs, pharmacist review of all digoxin drug orders and labs is the intervention strategy selected. Based on my estimate of 1,200 patients who will receive digoxin, and an average duration of therapy of 8.33 days, I expect 10,000 digoxin orders next year. Each intervention will cost the hospital $10 for the lab and $5 to $9 of pharmacist time to review the order and lab (total $15 to $19/intervention; cost range $150,000 to $190,000). Because of the extensive review, I assume my intervention will be highly successful for "inhouse" digoxin orders, and estimate a success rate of 90%. However, I also assume a success rate as low as 65% to allow for ADEs that won't be detected because they may be related to digoxin prescriptions and lab values ordered after the patient was discharged.

For the ADEs related to noncompliance, the intervention strategy selected was patient counseling. All patients discharged from the hospital with more than four medications (3,000 patients expected next year) will be counseled by a nurse or pharmacy resident. Costs are predicted to range from $6 to $8 per intervention (based on a 15 to 20 minute counselling session between the pharmacist and patient). (Total cost: 3,000 x [$6.00 or $8.00] = $18,000 to $24,000.)

The effectiveness of this interventional strategy is difficult to predict, since there are many reasons why patients are noncompliant with their medications other than lack of knowledge. Therefore, I estimate that I'll be able to reduce noncompliance-related ADEs by between 30% and 50%.

Let's review the results. Table 3 shows the spreadsheet used to gather information and compute the results. The software program easily allows one to perform a sensitivity analysis by varying the intervention costs, benefits, and success rates. Note that for each alternative, sensitivity analysis was used to generate four possible alternatives: low costs and high benefits, high costs and high benefits, low costs and low benefits, and high costs and low benefits.

Targeting digoxin-related ADEs with direct pharmacist intervention results in the highest average net benefits ($16,000), with noncompliance-associated ADEs ranking second ($11,000) and ADEs associated with Dr Smith's patients ($4,500) ranking last. Based solely on the average numbers, it would appear that digoxin-related ADEs should be selected. However, the range of net benefits for digoxin-related ADEs is between $66,000 and negative $34,000. The risk of losing $34,000 may not be acceptable to this institution's management. In addition, the average ROI for this ADE category is 9%. If the institution must borrow funds at an interest rate higher than 9%, or demands that its projects generate an ROI greater than 9%, then this alternative would not be recommended.

How should one analyze the other ADE categories? The net benefits for targeting ADEs associated with Dr Smith's patients range from $9,500 to minus $500, with an average net benefit of $4,500 and an ROI of 25%. The net benefits for targeting noncompliance-related ADEs, on the other hand, range from $0 to $22,000, with an average net benefit of $11,000 and an ROI of 52%. The higher upside and a better downside of net benefits, and the higher ROI makes targeting noncompliance-associated ADEs clearly preferable to targeting the ADEs associated with Dr. Smith's patients.

Thus, if I had to select only one ADE scenario to target, I would target noncompliance, with use of patient counseling, as the intervention strategy. Despite the fact that it does not have the highest average net benefits, I would choose this option because of the lower volatility in the range of outcomes. However, some readers may have selected targeting digoxin-related ADEs, looking at the higher average net benefits, and the potential for a higher net benefit ($66,000 vs $22,000). In that case, an average ROI of 9% would have to be acceptable for this project in this institution.

CONCLUDING COMMENTS

The importance of using CBA can be seen by comparing it with other more simplistic models, in which different alternatives might have been selected. From a cost-minimization perspective, targeting the ADEs of Dr. Smith's patients would have been selected with an average cost of $18,000. If the objective had been to maximize benefits without regard to costs, then targeting digoxin-related ADEs offered the highest total benefits ($186,000 average).

In conclusion, the general rule to follow is to select the alternative that offers the highest average net benefits, unless either (a) the lower end of the range of expected net benefits would not be acceptable if it were to occur or (b) the ROI is unacceptably low given the institution's borrowing cost or required ROI on new projects. Finally, if two alternatives offer the same average or acceptable range of net benefits, select the one with the highest ROI.

In this chapter, we have seen how a technique of pharmacoeconomic analysis, cost-benefit analysis, was used to select the category of ADEs to be reduced, and the type of intervention. Despite different costs and benefits of alternatives, and the uncertainty associated with making estimates, use of cost-benefit analysis offers a strategy for deciding which ADEs would be best for your institution to target.

Using cost-effectiveness analysis to select drugs for therapeutic substitution

Learning Objectives:

After reading this chapter, one should be able to:

1. List different drug characteristics, and alternative economic, humanistic and clinical outcomes, by which the efficacy of drugs could be measured.

2. Calculate the cost-effectiveness ratio, and the incremental cost-effectiveness ratio, for one drug versus another.

3. Use cost-effectiveness analysis to select a drug suitable for therapeutic substitution.

This chapter is based on a question from reader Dr. RA, a pharmacy director in a community hospital in California. He wants to know how pharmacoeconomic analysis can be used to select agents for therapeutic substitution.

Therapeutic substitution involves selecting the drug of choice, from among alternatives, for a certain disease state or medical condition, which will be administered to the patient when one of the alternative drugs is ordered. The goal is to select the agent that provides an acceptable (but not necessarily the highest) level of effectiveness at the lowest possible cost.

Sometimes the decision process is easy. The ideal drug to select (if it exists) is the one that is both least expensive and most effective among alternative agents. Conversely, a drug not to select is one that is most expensive and least effective. The decision process gets trickier when a drug is either less expensive and less effective or more expensive and more effective.

How do you decide if the increase in effectiveness is worth the extra price you'll pay for the more expensive drug? For the less expensive drug, do the cost savings justify a lower rate of effectiveness? Pharmacoeconomic analysis is a tool to help you select the drugs in such cases by identifying which drug gives the most effectiveness per dollar spent.

Specifically, in this chapter, you'll learn how to collect and analyze cost-effectiveness information on drugs from different classes that have different costs and different degrees of effectiveness but which achieve the same therapeutic goal.

USING CEA IN THERAPEUTIC SUBSTITUTION DECISIONS: GENERAL PRINCIPLES

Cost-benefit analysis, which was discussed in the previous chapter, measures and compares multiple benefits simultaneously by converting all benefits into

| TABLE 1 | SELECTED DRUG CHARACTERISTICS AND OUTCOMES THAT CAN BE COMPARED USING COST-EFFECTIVENESS ANALYSIS |

Drug characteristics
- Routes of administration
- Dosing frequency or duration
- Number of FDA approved indications
- Routes of drug elimination
- Number of drug-drug or drug-food interactions

Outcomes
- Decreased mortality
- Lower incidence of side effects (nausea, sedation, anticholinergic effects)
- Better cure rate for bacterial, fungal, or viral infection
- Lower incidence of chronic, disabling disease (stroke, congestive heart failure, emphysema)
- Improvement in lab "function" tests (liver, pulmonary, kidney)
- Improved primary lab tests (BP for antihypertensives, cholesterol for antihyperlipidemics, blood sugar for oral hypoglycemics)
- Improvement in quality of life (improved exercise tolerance, decreased depression, other psychosocial improvements, decreased pain)
- Better patient compliance expected

*Formulary/*Source: L. Basskin, PharmD

dollars. Cost-effectiveness analysis (CEA) only measures one dimension of effectiveness at a time. In cost-effectiveness analysis, the cost of therapy is divided by the nondollar (or natural units) of effectiveness being measured—e.g., units of blood pressure, number of lives saved, number of people cured. The goal is to select the drug with the lowest ratio of cost to effectiveness.

Some of the criteria that can be used to distinguish and compare the efficacy of two or more drugs under consideration for therapeutic substitution is shown in table 1. The relevant measurement selected depends on the perspective of the analysis (i.e., institution, patient, society), the relative priorities of the study coordinator, the ease with which the effectiveness or efficacy information can be collected, the patient population at the study institution, and the specific reason for therapeutic substitution (e.g., if the goal of therapeutic substitution is to identify agents that can be switched from IV to oral or used by more outpatients, patient compliance could be used as the measure of effectiveness).

Before discussing this chapter's question on therapeutic substitution, let's gain some basic understanding of the concepts of cost-effectiveness ratios and cost per life saved. Examine table 2. Three alternative drugs are available for use, all of which save lives. Assume that the number of lives saved is the only difference in effectiveness between them.

Drug A is clearly not preferable, as it is both the most expensive and least effective. Drug B appears to be the agent that should be selected, as it has the

TABLE 2	**COMPARISON OF COST-EFFECTIVENESS RATIOS OF THREE FICTITIOUS DRUGS**		
Drug	**Cost to treat 100 patients**	**Lives saved per 100 patients treated**	**Cost-effectiveness ratio (Dollars per life saved)**
A	$30,000	1	$30,000
B	6,000	3	2,000
C	22,000	5	4,500

Formulary/Source: L. Basskin, PharmD

lowest cost-effectiveness ratio. But what about drug C? The cost-effectiveness ratio for drug C is higher than drug B, but it also saves more lives.

Using a simple formula, it is easy to calculate the extra cost of one more unit of effectiveness—divide the differences in costs of the two drugs by the differences in their efficacy. In this case, ($22,000 minus $6,000) ÷ (5 minus 3 lives) it is $8,000 per life saved. Another way to look at this is to say that if 100 patients were treated with drug C instead of drug A, two extra lives would be saved and the cost per extra life saved would be $8,000.

Is this a reasonable price to pay? This is a decision each institution will have to wrestle with. Whenever you get more effectiveness for a price, one has to decide if the additional costs represent "fair value." Some pharmacoeconomists and public health economists have argued that, from a societal perspective, up to $30,000 per year of life saved is an acceptable price to pay. In our example, if patients taking drug C lived for 5 more years, the cost would be ($8,000 ÷ 5 years) $1,600 per year, a price that would appear to be reasonable to pay.

However, what if the drug saved a life but only extended it by less than a year, and that year was spent in intensive care? Is it still worth $8,000 to save that life? These are tough questions to answer, but pharmacoeconomic analysis can at least provide the number of dollars that must be spent to gain that extra unit of effectiveness.

Typically, published studies that present mortality data only provide the percentage survival rate. Keep in mind that an easy way to compare the cost-effectiveness of two drugs is to assume that 100 patients will be treated and to calculate the costs and effectiveness for this number of patients. For example, assume drugs X and Y cost $100 and $150, respectively, and have survival rates of 80% and 90%, respectively. If 100 patients were treated, drug X would cost $10,000 and save 80 patients. Drug Y would cost $15,000 and save 90 patients. The difference in the cost-effectiveness ratio is ($15,000 minus $10,000) ÷ (90 minus 80 lives saved) $500 per life saved.

STEPS IN PERFORMING CEA

Before examining this chapter's question on use of pharmacoeconomics in therapeutic substitution, review the steps involved with performing cost-effectiveness analyses. The steps are to:

1. Identify the perspective of the analysis.

EXHIBIT 1

Efficacy or effectiveness: Which is which?

The terms "efficacy" and "effectiveness" are often used interchangeably; however, there is a difference between them. I view efficacy as the ability of a drug to achieve a measurable endpoint or desired effect, while effectiveness is the ability of the drug to result in a positive therapeutic outcome in the "real population."

In a typical controlled study, the drug's *efficacy* (or its ability to achieve its desired effect in a controlled environment), can be evaluated by controlling all other extraneous variables and omitting people from the study whose other diseases or conditions might prevent the drug from accomplishing the goal. *Effectiveness* is the ability of a drug to accomplish those goals under real-life conditions, in a more realistic patient population with other concurrent diseases that might affect the drug's ability to work.

Typically, more efficacy than effectiveness studies are published in the medical and pharmacy literature. However, what most clinicians want to know and what often must be extrapolated from these studies is the drug's effectiveness in relevant patient populations. For example, certain antihypertensive drugs have been shown to be efficacious at reducing blood pressure. However, efficacy studies often don't examine which of these drugs is more effective in hypertensive patients with concomitant diseases nor do they address other important outcomes such as reduction in mortality. Sometimes the answers to these questions can best be obtained by conducting your own effectiveness studies.

2. Identify the drugs you wish to compare.

3. Determine the cost of each drug.

4. Select the measure of effectiveness by which the drugs will be compared.

5. From outside studies or from your own facility's information, determine the efficacy or effectiveness of each drug (see exhibit 1 for definition of these terms).

6. Calculate the cost-effectiveness ratio for each drug. Use sensitivity analysis as appropriate.

7. Compare the differences in cost-effectiveness ratios between the drugs included in the analysis.

8. Select the drug for therapeutic substitution.

USING CEA IN THERAPEUTIC SUBSTITUTION DECISIONS: COMPARING THREE ANTIEMETICS

Let's apply these steps to evaluate the therapeutic substitution of a specific example—antiemetics to prevent postop emesis. Relevant information and a summary of the cost-effectiveness analysis of three unnamed but real drugs that have different dosing regimens, costs, and reported efficacy are shown in table 3.

After deciding on the perspective from which to measure costs and bene-

TABLE 3	CALCULATION OF COST-EFFECTIVENESS INFORMATION OF THREE ANTIEMETIC AGENTS			
		Drug A	**Drug B**	**Drug C**
Drug cost/dose		$6.00	$2.00	$0.25
Administration cost/dose		$5.00	$2.50	$0.25
Total cost/dose		$11.00	$4.50	$0.50
Doses per day		2	3	4
Total cost/day		$22.00	$13.50	$2.00
No. of postop patient-days/year patients will receive antiemetics for postop nausea and vomiting		15,000	15,000	15,000
Total annual drug cost		$330,000	$202,500	$30,000
Efficacy in preventing emesis	Low	90%	80%	70%
	High	100%	90%	95%
	Average	95%	85%	83%
Emetic episodes avoided*	Worst	4.50	4.00	3.50
	Best	5.00	4.50	4.75
	Average	4.75	4.25	4.13
Cost-effectiveness ratio†	Worst	$4.89	$3.38	$0.57
	Best	$4.40	$3.00	$0.42
	Average	$4.64	$3.19	$0.50

* Assumes average of five emetic episodes per patient per day.
† Cost per emetic episode avoided.

Formulary/Source: L. Basskin, PharmD

fits, collect each drug's acquisition and administration costs, and note each drug's frequency of administration.

Annual drugs costs are calculated based on a projected number of postop days in the next year patients will receive antiemetics for nausea and vomiting. In this example, based on our predicted census for next year, we projected that there will be 15,000 postop patient-days next year. A chart review of a sample of postop patients also indicated an average of five episodes of emesis per day occurred in patients who received no antiemetics at all.

The measurement of effectiveness selected for this example of therapeutic substitution is reduction in emetic episodes. In our example, this information was derived from the medical and pharmacy literature. A better source of this data–particularly if time and resources are available—would be to conduct a retrospective or concurrent study of the actual usage patterns and outcomes

TABLE 4 — COMPARISON OF DIFFERENCES IN COST-EFFECTIVENESS RATIOS USING SENSITIVITY ANALYSIS FOR PREVENTING EMESIS

	Five scenarios comparing the efficacy of drug C versus drug A				
Efficacy of drug C in avoiding emetic episodes*	Best 4.75	Best 4.75	Worst 3.50	Worst 3.50	Average 4.13
Efficacy of drug A in avoiding emetic episodes*	Worst 4.50	Best 5.00	Worst 4.50	Best 5.00	Average 4.75
Extra (fewer) emetic episodes with drug C versus drug A†	(3,750)	3,750	15,000	22,500	9,300
Cost per emetic episode avoided if drug A is selected over drug C‡	N/A	$80.00	$20.00	$13.33	$32.26

	Five scenarios comparing the efficacy of drug C versus drug B				
Efficacy of drug C avoiding emetic episodes*	Best 4.75	Best 4.75	Worst 3.50	Worst 3.50	Average 4.13
Efficacy of drug B avoiding emetic episodes*	Worst 4.00	Best 4.50	Worst 4.00	Best 4.50	Average 4.25
Extra (fewer) emetic episodes with drug C versus drug B†	(11,250)	(3,750)	7,500	15,000	1,875
Cost per emetic episode avoided if drug B is selected over drug C‡	N/A	N/A	$23.00	$11.50	$92.00

* Data from table 3.

† Equal to 15,000 patient-days per year (from table 3) x difference in emetic episodes avoided between the two drugs. For example, the calculation of column two's entry when comparing drug C vs drug A is 15,000 x (4.75 minus 5.00) = 3,750.

‡ Equal to the difference in cost per day of the two drugs (from table 3) divided by the difference in emetic episodes per day between the two drugs. For example, the calculation of column two's entry when comparing drug C vs drug A is ($22.00 minus $2.00) ÷ (4.75 minus 5.00) = $80.00.

Formulary/Source: L. Basskin, PharmD

of these medications in your own facility.

In our example, drug A must be given by slow infusion twice daily, and costs $6.00 per dose. Administration costs related to the drug include an IV fluid piggyback, pump, and preparation time (based on the average hourly salary of technician) total $5.00/dose. The drug reduces the incidence of emetic episodes by 90% to 100%.

Drug B can be given by slow IV push and does not require dilution. It costs $2.00/dose and must be given three times daily. Its administration costs include nurse delivery time of $2.50 (based on the average nurse salary and average delivery time). The drug is moderately effective, with efficacy results ranging from 80% to 90%.

Drug C is inexpensive ($0.25/ dose), dosed four times daily, and administration costs are the syringe and needle only (also $0.25/dose). Its efficacy in reducing emetic episodes is variable, ranging from 70% to 95%.

The next step in a cost-effectiveness analysis is to convert the percentage efficacy data into the number of emesis episodes avoided each day (multiply the five episodes per day times the percentage efficacy—i.e., the low, high, and average outcome scenarios).

Next, calculate the cost-effectiveness ratio, or cost per emetic episode avoided, by dividing the total drug cost per day by the number of emetic incidents avoided daily, based on worst, best, and average efficacy.

Drug C is clearly the most cost-effective, with costs ranging from $0.42 to $0.57/episode avoided. Furthermore, drug C is associated with annual cost savings to the institution of $300,000 ($330,000 minus $30,000) and $172,500 ($202,500 minus $30,000) if it is chosen over drugs A and B, respectively.

Some pharmacoeconomists might stop their analysis at this point and select drug C as their antiemetic agent of choice, recommending therapeutic substitution of drugs A and B with drug C. However, I think there is another step that needs to be taken before ruling out the use of drugs A or B.

Even though drugs A and B have higher cost-effectiveness ratios, your facility's administration may be willing to pay the higher cost if it results in cost savings elsewhere in your health care system. If each episode of emesis requires a further intervention, or delays the discharge of the patient, there is a cost to the institution. Therefore, I determine the *difference* in cost-effectiveness ratios of drugs A and B versus drug C to determine the cost of obtaining the higher efficacy associated with these drugs. I'll also perform a sensitivity analysis, comparing the best outcomes of drug C with the worse outcomes of drugs A and B (and vice versa), to determine how these different outcomes affect my decision (table 4).

There are two ways to calculate the difference in cost-effectiveness ratios. The first method has already been presented in this column—i.e., divide the difference in daily costs between the two drugs by the difference in each drug's efficacy. For example, using average efficacies for drugs A and C, this equals $32.26 per emetic episode avoided ($22.00/day minus $2.00/day) ÷ (4.75 episodes/day minus 4.13 episodes/day). This $32.26 represents the extra cost my institution would pay per emetic episode to reduce the number of episodes per year by a further 9,300 (15,000 patient-days x [4.75 minus 4.13 episodes per patient day]).

The other way of calculating this comparison is to determine the extra number of emetic episodes that would result over a year based on using drug C over drug A or B. This is calculated as the number of days per year patients will receive antiemetics (15,000) times the decrease in efficacy of using drug C. For example, again using the average efficacy of drug C and drug A, the number of extra emetic episodes per year incurred with drug C would be

9,300. Then divide the extra yearly cost of using drug A ($300,000) by the emetic episodes incurred with drug C to get the same $32.26 per emetic episode. I perform these calculations using computer software that allows me to play "what-if" scenarios and change the cost or efficacy to see how the scenario changes.

Note that for drug A in the first column of the five scenarios shown in table 4 and for drug B in the first and second columns, I've marked N/A (for not applicable) rather than perform the calculations. Since drug costs are higher and efficacy is lower in each of these three cases, these drugs would never be preferable selections over drug C.

As shown in table 4, the difference in cost efficacy ranges from $13.33 to $80.00 for drug A and from $11.50 to $92.00 for drug B. I must now decide if these amounts are reasonable to pay for the cost of preventing an extra emesis episode.

How? One way is to relate it to the extra costs to the facility associated with an extra emetic episode, such as an increased length of stay in the postop recovery area, or the cost of a physician intervention, or even the cost of a dissatisfied patient as it might affect the institution's attempts to build a patient base.

CONCLUSION

Cost-effectiveness analysis is a pharmacoeconomic tool that allows one to select an agent for therapeutic substitution based on the lowest cost-effectiveness ratio. When another drug has a higher cost-effectiveness ratio but is more effective, calculate the extra cost of increasing the efficacy by one unit, and decide if this amount is a "reasonable price" to pay for the added efficacy or effectiveness.

Using cost-utility analysis to select which clinical pharmacy services to offer

Learning Objectives:
After reading this chapter, one should be able to:

1. Define and rank the most important objectives to be satisfied from provision of a specific clinical service, from a given perspective.

2. Calculate the cost/patient and cumulative costs to the healthcare institution, of providing a clinical service to patients.

3. Use cost-utility analysis to evaluate, and select from among, alternative clinical services.

One of the questions I frequently encounter is how to use pharmacoeconomics to show the value or benefits from providing clinical pharmacy services. In this month's column, I'll show you how to use cost-utility analysis to evaluate clinical pharmacy services by comparing the costs to a measure of the multiple benefits of providing those services.

In many settings, clinical pharmacy services are offered based both on the explicit need and request of the physician. There's no limit to the number of clinical services that can be offered. Some common clinical services are shown in table 1.

Usually, there is not an organized approach to determining the cost of providing that service or a quantification of the benefits that will result. Most published pharmacoeconomic studies evaluate a single outcome measurement with a single service, like patient satisfaction and pain management or incidence of bleeding and anticoagulant monitoring, and try to show that having the pharmacist monitor and/or intervene in the patient's drug therapy is a cost-effective way of caring for that patient.

These studies are an excellent starting point, though they have a serious limitation. They often use cost-benefit analysis, which requires that all benefits be converted into dollars, an extremely difficult task, or they use cost-effectiveness analysis, which allows for the comparison of costs with only one nondollar measure of outcome, such as lives saved.

Since it is difficult to measure the impact of a clinical pharmacy service on even one objective, let alone several, these pharmacoeconomic tools are difficult to apply to this scenario. More specifically, some of the reasons why a different pharmacoeconomic model is needed to evaluate clinical pharmacy services include the following:

- Each service has a different cost based on the time required to provide

EXHIBIT 1

Why offer clinical services?

Many reasons can be given as to why one should offer clinical pharmacy services. Among the reasons are to improve therapeutic outcomes, reduce the inconvenience of phone calls and other intrusions on physicians' time, and enhance the profile of the pharmacy department among physicians and patients. Here are some other objectives I considered for providing these services:

■ Decrease the cost of therapy.
■ Decrease length of stay.
■ Avoid adverse drug events (due to renal failure, drug interactions, drug levels outside the therapeutic range).
■ Decrease readmissions to the hospital.
■ Increase patient satisfaction.
■ Increase exposure and/or profile of pharmacists to physicians.
■ Educate prescribers.
■ Increase the volume and/or number of patients seen.
■ Meet a perceived need of physicians not met elsewhere.
■ Meet a perceived need of patients not met elsewhere.

it and necessary laboratory tests.

■ Each service has a different number of patients and physicians who benefit.

■ Each service achieves a different set of objectives to a different degree.

■ Depending on the perspective of the user, some objectives are more important than others.

■ The benefits of providing clinical services are both tangible (e.g., shortened length of stay) and intangible (e.g., patient satisfaction).

■ Some objectives are easily measurable or quantifiable in dollars, while others are not.

ADAPTING COST-ANALYSIS PRINCIPLES TO A STEP-BY-STEP MODEL

To account for these problems, I've developed a new model based on cost-utility analysis principles. It is similar to cost-effectiveness analysis except that the measure of utility, unlike effectiveness, is a composite of more than one factor. The steps involved in working with this model are as follows:

1. Identify the clinical services to be considered.

2. Select the study perspective.

3. Identify the relevant goals and objectives of providing the clinical services from that perspective.

4. For each service under consideration, rank or measure the ability of that service to satisfy that objective.

5. Add up the number of objectives that will be satisfied for each service.

6. Estimate the cost of providing that service (usually based on clinician's time and hourly rate, and laboratory costs).

TABLE 1 CLINICAL AREAS FOR WHICH SERVICES CAN BE PROVIDED

- Acute emergency/ critical care patients (monitoring drug therapy)
- Acute pain management (e.g., postop)
- ADE monitoring (concurrent)
- Aminoglycoside, vancomycin, PK monitoring
- Antibiotic therapy (C & S, empiric therapy)
- Anticoagulant therapy (education)
- Anticoagulant therapy (monitoring)
- Anticonvulsant therapy (education)
- Anticonvulsant therapy (monitoring)
- Cardiac patients (education)
- Cardiac patients (monitoring)
- Candidates for likely readmission

- Chronic pain management (e.g., cancer)
- Chronic renal failure patients (making dosing recommendations)
- Diabetic patients (education)
- Discharge counseling
- Drug histories on admission
- Meds that are expensive
- Meds with high risk of toxicity
- Nutrition—TPN, enteral, feeding tubes (reviewing orders)
- Patients identified as noncompliant
- Pediatric consults
- Pharmacist addition to the code blue team
- Polypharmacy
- Psychiatric patients (education)
- Psychiatric patients (monitoring)
- Pulmonary patients (education)
- Pulmonary patients (monitoring)
- Surgery consults

*Formulary/*Source: L. Basskin, PharmD

7. Estimate the number of interventions or patients to be seen by that service.

8. Divide the cost per intervention for each service by the respective number of objectives met, to derive a *cost per objective ratio.*

9. Multiply the number of interventions per year by the number of objectives met to determine the total number of objectives met per year.

10. Multiply the total number of interventions by the cost per intervention to obtain the service's total cost per year.

11. Select the service(s) with the lowest cost per objective and whose total time or cost will not exceed the time or expense that the institution is willing to make available (i.e., cost of service does not exceed the available resources).

SELECTION OF CLINICAL PHARMACY SERVICES: DATA COLLECTION

To provide a practical example, let's look at a situation I recently faced. The hospital at which I practice wanted to expand the number of clinical services provided by the pharmacy department. After developing a list of 10 possible services, I met with nurses, patients, physicians, and hospital administration and narrowed the list to 4 choices.

There were two major constraints on selecting the services to be offered.

TABLE 2 PHARMACOECONOMIC COMPARISON OF FOUR CLINICAL PHARMACY SERVICES

Calculation of the average number of objectives met from providing a clinical service

Objective of service*	Pain management	TPN monitoring	Heparin monitoring	Code blue team
Decrease length of stay	3	1	1	2
Meets physician need	4	2	4	4
Decreases drug costs	1	4	2	3
Increases patient satisfaction	4	0	0	4
Decreases adverse drug event incidence	4	2	4	1
Total score (max 20)	16	9	11	14
Number of objectives met[†] (max score 5)	4	2.25	2.75	3.5

Calculation of cost per objective, total objectives met, and total cost

	Pain management	TPN monitoring	Heparin monitoring	Code blue team
No. minutes per intervention (incl. lab review, patient consult, chart documentation)	12	25	10	30
Average hourly salary of clinical pharmacist	$30.00	$30.00	$30.00	$30.00
Cost per intervention[‡]	$6.00	$12.50	$5.00	$15.00
No. of objectives met	4	2.25	2.75	3.5
Cost per objective met[§]	$1.50	$5.56	$1.82	$4.29
No. interventions per year	4,200	3,650	20,400	1,100
Total objectives met per year[‖]	16,800	8,212	56,100	3,850
Total cost per year[¥]	$25,200	$45,625	$102,000	$16,500
Total FTEs required per year	0.4	0.7	1.7	0.3

* Each service was ranked from 0 to 4 regarding its ability and likelihood to satisfy that objective from the perspective of the hospital
   0 = highly unlikely; 1 = unlikely; 2 = neutral; 3 = likely; and 4 = highly likely
† = Initial scoring of objectives was from 0 to 4. These scores need to be divided by four so that the maximum score for any one objective is
   1.0, and the maximum total is 5.0 for the five objectives (five objectives x 1.0)
‡ = Calculated as average hourly salary ÷ 60 minutes per hour x no. of minutes per intervention
§ = Calculated as cost per intervention ÷ no. of objectives met
‖ = Calculated as no. of interventions per year x no. of objectives met
¥ = Calculated as cost per intervention x total no. of interventions per year

Formulary/Source: L. Basskin, PharmD

No more than 0.7 FTEs could be added at this time, and the service had to be made available to all patients and physicians in the hospital.

Identification. The four services selected for further evaluation were pain management (PCA monitoring), total parental nutrition monitoring (reviewing all labs and recommending orders), heparin monitoring (reviewing labs for patients on heparin and recommending changes), and acting as a member of the existing code blue team (i.e., responding to code blues, preparing drugs for distribution, and making drug recommendations).

Perspective. Since hospital administration wanted services to primarily benefit the hospital, I chose the perspective of the hospital for measuring costs and effectiveness.

Goals. The objectives to be achieved through expansion of clinical services were to:

- decrease patient length of stay,
- meet a need of the physician not met elsewhere,
- decrease drug costs in the hospital, and
- increase patient satisfaction, and decrease the incidence of adverse drug events (ADEs).

Ranking of services/objectives met per service. Each service was ranked from 0 to 4 regarding the ability and likelihood of that objective being satisfied from the perspective of the hospital (0 = highly unlikely, 1 = unlikely, 2 = neutral, 3 = likely, and 4 = highly likely). The ranking scores were obtained by asking all pharmacists and a selected number of other health care professionals to rank each of the services in terms of likelihood to meet the objectives after describing the content and purpose of each service. The process of seeking consensus from experts in this manner is known as a *Delphi* panel or technique.

The scores for each objective and service combination were averaged, and average scores for all objectives were then totaled for each service (see table 2). The number was divided by 4 so that the maximum score for any service and any one objective would be 1.0. The maximum total score, or number of objectives met from providing that service, would be 5.0 (i.e., five objectives × maximum score of 1.0 each).

Next, the average number of minutes required to provide each service was estimated. This information was obtained from various sources. For example, a literature review revealed average times required to intervene in a heparin service. The hospital had records showing the duration of a typical code blue to be 30 minutes. I relied on my personal experience with TPN monitoring and pain management services to estimate the daily time required.

Number of interventions. The estimate of the number of patient interventions were based on hospital records. In the preceding year, there were 1,100 code blues. From the pharmacy data base, it was determined that an average of 10 TPNs were ordered and prepared each day (Total for the year: 3,650). For patient-controlled analgesia (PCA) use, records in the pharmacy data base revealed that 2,100 patients per year each used a PCA for an average of 2 days (4,200 patient days), and from personal experience, I assumed that at least one intervention would be required per patient per day.

The estimate of heparin interventions was more difficult. I knew the duration of heparin therapy (4 days) and number of patients who received heparin last year (2,914). I assumed that interventions would be required both on a scheduled basis and whenever the patient's activated partial thromboplastin time (aPTT) was not within the therapeutic range. I knew the number of relevant labs (aPTTs) last year, but I did not believe that all labs were necessary, or were being properly ordered.

A literature review indicated that labs are generally taken every 6 hours after changes to the heparin infusion rate, and then daily thereafter. Infusion rates are changed until the patient reaches goal aPTT. I assumed it would take 1 day for the patient to reach the goal aPTT. Therefore, the number of interventions was assumed to be four for the first day of therapy and one for every day thereafter. Based on an average duration of heparin therapy of 4 days, and 2,914 patients who received heparin last year, I calculated 20,400 interventions for the year ([2,914 patients × 4 interventions on day 1 = 11,656], plus 1 intervention on each of days 2 through 4 [2,914 × 3 days = 8,742]).

In the cost category, I only included the cost of the clinician's time to check the laboratory findings, monitor the patient, and document the intervention. I assumed that the number of laboratory tests would not change if the service were in place.

SELECTION OF CLINICAL PHARMACY SERVICES: WEIGHING THE OPTIONS

Examination of costs. Let's examine the results, looking at the pros and cons of each service. The code blue team requires the least amount of FTEs (0.3), costs only $16,500 per year, and meets the second highest number of objectives (3.5). However, it has the highest cost per intervention ($15.00) and the second highest cost per objective ($4.29).

Heparin monitoring has the second lowest cost per objective ($1.82) and would result in the highest number of interventions (20,400), but at a cost of 1.7 FTEs, it is over the budget given to me (i.e., could allocate no more than 0.7 FTEs).

Monitoring TPN can be completed within the budgeted number of FTEs. However, by virtue of its low number of objectives met (2.25) and the second highest cost per intervention ($12.50), it has the highest cost per objective ($5.56).

Pain management has the lowest cost per objective ($1.50) and the highest number of objectives met (4.0). It will require 0.4 FTEs and result in 16,800 objectives being satisfied annually—which is more than the TPN monitoring or the code blue team option.

Recommendation. My recommendation was to expand the clinical services being offered at my hospital in two areas: pain management and the code blue team. The total required number of FTEs of 0.7 for these two services was within the budget, with an average cost per objective of $2.02 per objective ([$25,200 + 16,500]/[16,800 + 3,850]). While heparin monitoring, with a cost per objective of $1.82, is more cost-effective than either code blue or the combination of code blue and pain management, I have the constraint of not being able to afford to offer the service to the whole hospital. Additionally, this option was over my FTE allowance of 0.7. Therefore, since I couldn't split off 0.3 FTE for the heparin service, I added the 0.3 FTE from code blue to the 0.4 FTE from pain management in order to fully utilize the 0.7 FTE allocated to us.

As an alternative to adding code blue (and its higher cost per objective) to utilize the 0.7 FTEs, I suggested to the administrative group that the constraints be relaxed to allow us to offer pain management to all patients and heparin monitoring to a smaller group of select patients. This would enable both the pain management service and 0.3 FTE's worth of the heparin monitoring service to be performed within budget, which would maximize the number of objectives by choosing the most cost-effective services.

By incorporating this model on spreadsheet software, sensitivity analysis can be employed to play "what if" scenarios and vary such factors as the number of minutes per intervention, or number of interventions required per patient, to determine how the relative results change.

For simplicity sake, in this model each objective was assumed to be of equal importance, so that the "effectiveness" score was a simple sum of the number of objectives met. However, in most cases, the provision of each clinical service will not be viewed as being of equal importance to the user of the study. You could modify this model by "weighting" the different objectives—the average scores (divided by four) would be multiplied by an "importance factor" of 1 to 10. By summing this information, you could calculate the *weighted objectives met* and *total number of weighted objectives met for the year.* You could then conduct sensitivity analysis to determine how the results change as the weighting factors are changed.

CONCLUDING COMMENTS

In this chapter, I showed you how cost-utility analysis and this new model can be used to determine the cost and benefits per patient as well as the total cost of providing a service. It can also be used as a tool to select services that maximize the benefits by satisfying the greatest number of clinical objectives.

Using cost-effectiveness analysis to analyze and select drugs for use in surgery

Learning Objectives:
After reading this chapter, one should be able to:

1. Identify and list the key characteristics of, and difficulties in analyzing economically, medications associated with surgery.

2. Determine the total and average healthcare costs of treating undesirable or toxic effects from the use of a specific drug or class of drugs.

3. Use cost-benefit analysis to evaluate the extent to which different drugs achieve desirable outcomes (or avoid undesirable outcomes) and to select alternatives for a given category of surgery-related drugs.

EW, a pharmacy director in Washington wants to know how pharmacoeconomic analysis can be used to evaluate drug selections in surgery. EW is not alone in wondering how these drug costs can be analyzed. There are several reasons why this area of medicine causes the pharmacy department concern, not the least of which is evaluating drug costs.

It is important to control drug use throughout a health care facility, and the technique of pharmacoeconomic analysis described in this column is applicable to drug therapy regardless of the location of the drugs or the nature of the prescriber. Surgery, however, has many unique barriers that make drug selection, evaluation, and monitoring a difficult task (see Exhibit 1). Despite these complexities, there *is* a systematic approach one can take to reviewing the cost-effectiveness of drugs used in surgery.

In this chapter, I'll share *my* approach to analyzing drug costs related to surgery. Using the example of prophylactic anticoagulation, I'll present the steps I believe one should take to conduct a pharmacoeconomic analysis in this field; namely, to analyze one class of surgical drugs at a time. Keep in mind that it is the rational approach or *process* that is important to learn through the following example; the specific results are not important and should not be extrapolated to your practice setting.

STEPS TO DETERMINING THE COST-EFFECTIVENESS OF DRUGS USED IN SURGERY

After first identifying an area of drug therapy for surgical patients in which alternatives exist, the goals of this type of pharmacoeconomic analysis should be to evaluate and compare the cost-effectiveness of alternative agents in order to make a recommendation. It is not necessary that there be only one alternative recommended for all surgical procedures. The same therapeutic problem might have different solutions depending on criteria such as the patient's sex or age, type of surgery, concurrent disease states or medications, or the duration of surgery.

When determining the class of drugs for consideration, it may be more useful to group drugs by their therapeutic use, rather than by the same "chemical class." Also, while it is true that drug use differs subtly between surgeries, there are many drug needs or categories common to most surgeries. Major categories of therapy include prophylactic anticoagulants and antibiotics, neuromuscular blockers, postoperative analgesics, postoperative antiemetics, and anesthetic agents.

I recommend the following nine-step approach as a means to evaluate the cost-effectiveness of drug use in the surgical setting.

Consider the therapeutic issue and alternatives. Before conducting the economic analysis, it is important to first understand the pharmacologic and physiologic issues related to surgery. One doesn't gain credibility with physicians by making purely cost-minimization recommendations without understanding what alternative treatments exist and why one alternative is more effective than another.

In my example, the issue is whether or not prophylactic anticoagulation is necessary in certain surgical procedures. Two risks associated with major surgery are the development of deep venous thrombosis (DVT) and pulmonary embolism (PE). While several well-designed studies have shown that use of prophylactic anticoagulants for certain categories of surgical patients reduces the incidence of DVT and PE, these agents also increase the risk of bleeding.

Issues surrounding anticoagulant use involve the length of therapy prior to and following surgery, their relative effectiveness at preventing DVT and PE, the specific types of surgeries for which anticoagulation is recommended, and the risk of bleeding associated with alternative therapies such as warfarin, subcutaneous heparin (SQH), and the newer low molecular weight heparins (LMWH). While the LMWHs have been shown in some studies to be at least as, if not more, effective and require less monitoring than oral warfarin, SQH, or intravenous heparin, pharmacoeconomic analysis is necessary to determine if the extra cost of LMWHs can be justified.

The goal of the present analysis was to determine which, if any, drug should be used for DVT/PE prophylaxis prior to surgery. Rather than considering all surgeries and the varying risks of DVT/PE, I considered two specific procedures for which there were (1) reports in the literature of a higher incidence of DVT/PE, and (2) a variety of drug therapies being used by surgeons in our hospital.

To accomplish this goal, three questions had to be answered as they related to our patient population and our institution's drug costs. (1) Was there really a reduction in the risk of DVT/PE if prophylaxis was used? (2) Were the benefits of prophylaxis greater than the costs of drug toxicities (e.g., bleeding)? (3) If the benefits of drug therapy exceeded their costs, which of the alternative agents was the most cost-effective and should be recommended for use?

Based on a discussion with physicians and nurses of possible problematic

EXHIBIT 1

Pharmacoeconomic challenges unique to the surgical setting

The pharmacy has less control over drug use and custody.

For most drugs, pharmacists maintain physical control of the drugs and are usually able to review the drug orders for appropriateness before the drug is dispensed or administered to the patient. However, anesthesiology is often the one specialty within the hospital that maintains custody of its drugs. In addition, there is often reluctance to recommend changes to "preprinted, standing surgical orders," and it is difficult to standardize drug use with the multitude of "standing drug orders" in use by different surgeons for the same surgical procedures.

Barriers exist that prevent easy evaluation of patient response to several drug categories used in surgery.

These barriers include:

■ The short duration—often only minutes—of drugs used in the surgical setting generally requires either direct viewing of the patient or concurrent data collection to assess response. This is not conducive to the typical "retrospective chart review" conducted by many institutions to evaluate drug use.

■ The "closed door" policy of the operating room and the sterile clothing requirement prevent quick and easy patient access and drug use evaluation.

■ Many of the drugs used in surgery are designed to prevent postoperative complications or result in improvements not immediately noticeable in the inpatient setting. In most institutions, there is no postdischarge follow-up mechanism in place, making it difficult to evaluate the effectiveness of different medications. Moreover, since the patient with complications may be admitted to a different hospital, or not admitted at all, a reliable source of information about the costs of drug side effects or postoperative complications is unavailable.

procedures, two procedures considered for review were knee surgery and abdominal surgery. Alternatives evaluated were use of no drugs or use of warfarin, SQH, or LMWH.

Select the perspective of the analysis. The next step in the analysis is to select a perspective from which all costs and outcomes will be measured. From the options of societal, patient, institution, and physician, the institutional perspective was chosen for the example described in this article.

Identify the patient population affected. Before selecting patient charts to review, it is critical to identify the patient population to whom the results will be applied. In any analysis or study, the goal is to develop patient inclusion and exclusion criteria that mirror the ultimate users of the drug. By controlling a study's entry criteria, the effects of the drugs can be more clearly identified; however, the results of the study may not be applicable to patients who didn't meet the criteria.

An alternative strategy is to enroll patients who are more typical of the patient population (with their multiple medication regimens and concurrent diseases) and evaluate drug effectiveness in this group. The disadvantage of this approach is that if a large enough sample is not initially enrolled, one or two patients with adverse drug outcomes can skew results and lead to erroneously drawn conclusions.

In my study, I chose the latter approach and modified it slightly. I wanted to make recommendations that would be useful for the typical patients in my institution undergoing this type of surgery. However, I excluded patients who were already receiving warfarin chronically and those with a history of DVT or other thromboembolic disorders, as I thought these patient groups might generate results reflective of something other than the therapy being evaluated. I used statistical analysis to ensure that the sample size would be large enough to detect a difference between the groups, if one existed.

Select the pharmacoeconomic model. The pharmacoeconomic models to use in the surgical setting are either cost-minimization analysis (alternatives with the lowest costs), cost-effectiveness analysis (alternative with lowest cost/unit of efficacy ratio), or cost-benefit analysis (alternative with the highest net benefits, defined as the benefits less costs). Selection of CMA is most useful when alternative therapies are all thought to result in equivalent outcomes; CEA should be selected when there is only one nondollar outcome being evaluated, and CBA can be used when there is more than one outcome, but all outcomes can either be measured in or converted to dollars.

Even though I could have selected CEA, with an outcome of no surgical complications, I chose CBA because all of the outcomes (both positive and negative) can either be measured in or converted to dollars. I defined benefits as the savings resulting from decreased costs of DVT/PE treatment.

Select outcomes to measure. When evaluating alternative drug therapies, it is important to identify the outcome by which the relative effectiveness of the drugs will be measured. It is not enough just to say that drug A is better or more effective than drug B. Possible outcomes of drugs used in surgery include higher cure rate, decreased mortality, better side effect profile, improved quality of life and daily functioning, less pain or nausea, quicker onset of anesthesia, shorter time to extubation, and decreased postoperative complications of infection and coagulopathies.

In my example, the goal of this study was to identify cost-effective drugs to reduce the incidence of DVT or PE without bleeding complications in certain surgeries. One measurable outcome associated with an occurrence of DVT or PE was defined as a hospital admission requiring an intervention with heparin or surgery. A second outcome, related to the potential toxicity of these drugs, was to avoid serious bleeding. Bleeding complications were considered major if accompanied by a significant clinical event, a greater than 2 g/dl decrease in hemoglobin, or the need for transfusion of two or more units of blood products.

Identify the drug costs and outcomes. Once the outcomes are identified, calculate the costs and expected occurrence rates associated with each

TABLE 1 COSTS OF DRUG TOXICITY AND TREATMENT OF DVT/PE		
	Toxicity (bleeding)	**Inadequate prophylaxis (DVT/PE)**
Average number of ER visits	0.4	0.6
Marginal cost per ER visit	$440	$440
Expected cost	**$176**	**$264**
Average increase in length-of-stay	1.5	3
Marginal cost per day	$860	$860
Expected cost	**$1,290**	**$2,580**
Percentage of time surgery is required	15%	20%
Marginal cost of surgery	$2,850	$5,200
Expected cost	**$428**	**$1,040**
Drug therapy	**$325**	**$450**
Laboratory	**$175**	**$780**
Total costs	**$2,394**	**$5,114**

Formulary/Source: L. Basskin, PharmD

outcome. The costs of drug therapy include the cost of the drug and its administration and distribution, and the costs of inpatient drug therapy monitoring.

The costs of side effects and toxicities should also be determined. One deficiency of pharmacoeconomic analyses is that they fail to consider the costs of treating the adverse effects of drug therapy, concentrating only on measuring outcomes that are the *primary goal* of therapy.

For costs that occur less than 100% of the time, such as the cost of drug toxicities, calculate their "expected costs." The expected costs equals the cost of treating any event or outcome multiplied by its expected occurrence rate. For example, if treatment of a toxicity costs $5,000 and its occurrence rate is 5%, the expected cost of $250 ($5,000 × 5%) should be added to the cost of the drug therapy. While each person does not pay $250, over time, the average cost of treating that toxicity would be $250 per patient who receives that drug.

Table 1 shows the expected costs of an emergency room visit, a 1-day stay in the hospital, and cost of surgery for a patient who is either treated for bleeding or DVT or PE. Marginal costs of the ER visit and an increase in length of stay, which are defined as *expected average variable costs* (see Chapter 2 for further discussion), were calculated as *historic average variable costs* adjusted to take into account expected changes in costs and productivity at the hospital for next year.

The number of emergency visits and extra length of hospital stay, cost of laboratory and drug therapy, and percentage of time surgery was required was obtained from a review of both computerized records and charts of pa-

TABLE 2 WARFARIN, SUBCUTANEOUS HEPARIN, AND LOW MOLECULAR HEPARIN DRUG AND MONITORING COSTS			
	Warfarin	Subcutaneous heparin	Low molecular weight heparin
Drug acquisition cost	$0.50	$1.50	$28.50
Drug administration and delivery cost	$0.30	$0.50	$ 0.50
Total drug cost/dose	$0.80	$2.00	$29.00
Average No. of doses given	5	3	2
Drug cost per patient	**$4**	**$6**	**$58**
Monitoring costs per patient	**$100**	**$50**	**$0**

Formulary/Source: L. Basskin, PharmD

tients admitted through the emergency room for treatment of severe bleeding or DVT/PE.

The expected cost for each item was calculated as the incidence rate, or average duration, multiplied by the relevant cost. This number also equals the hospital's average cost per patient admitted for either severe bleeding or DVT/PE.

Table 2 depicts drug and monitoring costs associated with the three anti-coagulants used at my hospital. Drug costs were based on the hospital's ac-quisition costs while the number of doses was based on the average of all ap-plicable surgeons' preoperative and postoperative orders.

Laboratory monitoring costs were based on the assumed need for two lab-oratory values for patients receiving warfarin, one for patients receiving SQH, and none for those receiving LMWH. I used assumed laboratory monitoring information and relied on standing orders for drug use to minimize the amount of data collected from each patient's chart.

Although drug therapy was continued postoperatively for 7 to 14 days, these costs were incurred by the patient and were not included as costs from the hospital perspective. Accordingly, it is possible that an analysis performed from the perspective of the patient may have different results and reach dif-ferent conclusions.

Collect, sort, and analyze the data. Having identified the components of cost and effectiveness and the cost per component, one must now collect in-formation on the incidence of both the good outcomes (no incidence of DVT) and bad outcomes (major bleeding episodes).

There are three ways of obtaining the needed information. First, you could review the published results of randomized clinical trials involving the alter-natives medications. Second, you could conduct your own randomized clin-ical trial in your practice setting. Finally, you could conduct a retrospective chart review.

Each data collection method has its advantages and disadvantages. For ex-ample, although there is ample published information about the efficacy and toxicity of each of the three anticoagulant therapies used in this example, the

TABLE 3	RESULTS OF PATIENTS FOLLOWED FOR PROPHYLAXIS WITH ANTICOAGULANTS			
	No drugs	**Warfarin**	**Subcutaneous heparin**	**Low molecular weight heparin**
Number of patients:				
Knee surgery	25	51	75	32
Abdominal surgery	34	75	63	20
Total	59	126	138	52
Incidence of major bleeding:				
Knee surgery	1	5	6	3
Abdominal surgery	1	5	6	2
Total	2	10	12	5
Percentage incidence of major bleeding:				
Knee surgery	4.00%	9.80%	8.00%	9.38%
Abdominal surgery	2.94%	6.67%	9.52%	10.00%
Incidence of DVT/PE:				
Knee surgery	1	3	4	2
Abdominal surgery	9	6	4	1
Total	10	9	8	3
Percentage incidence of DVT/PE:				
Knee surgery	4.00%	5.88%	5.33%	6.25%
Abdominal surgery	26.47%	8.00%	6.35%	5.00%

Formulary/Source: L. Basskin, PharmD

studies don't adequately describe the patients at *my* institution nor address the surgeries I was interested in, so I used that information for background purposes only. Conducting a prospective, randomized clinical trial is ideal, but this strategy is often hampered by time, inconvenience, and cost.

Therefore, I chose a retrospective chart review as the data gathering method used in my example. I obtained a list of the 750 and 890 patients who underwent knee and abdominal surgery, respectively, in my hospital last year. From that list, I randomly selected a statistically sufficient number of patients and evaluated the selection of anticoagulant therapy (if any) and the incidence of DVT/PE and bleeding. If I had selected patients on the basis of adverse outcomes, or just those who received anticoagulant therapy, I would have biased my analysis by ignoring those patients who experienced no adverse outcomes or those who received or required no anticoagulation.

The results of the analysis are shown in table 3. A total of 365 charts of patients who underwent knee or abdominal surgery were reviewed. Since the number of patients undergoing each procedure were different, I calculated the percentage incidence of major bleeding and DVT/PE in each patient population.

I first evaluated the knee surgery data and found no statistically significant

TABLE 4	**COSTS OF DVT/PE PROPHYLAXIS FOR ABDOMINAL SURGERY***		

	Warfarin	Subcutaneous heparin	Low molecular weight heparin
Drug cost per patient (from table 2)	$4	$6	$58
Monitoring costs per patient (from table 2)	$100	$50	$0
Cost of toxicities (bleeds†) (from table 1)	$2,394	$2,394	$2,394
Percentage incidence with this drug less incidence with no drug (from table 3)	3.7%	6.6%	7.1%
Expected cost	$89	$158	$169
Total per patient costs‡	**$193**	**$214**	**$227**
Cost of DVT/PE (from table 1)	$5,114	$5,114	$5,114
Percentage incidence with this drug less incidence with no drug (from table 3)	18.5%	20.1%	21.5%
Expected savings	**$946**	**$1,027**	**$1,099**
Net benefit§	**$753**	**$813**	**$872**

*All costs rounded to nearest dollar
† Bleeding complications were considered major if accompanied by a significant clinical event, or greater than 2 g/dl decrease in hemoglobin, or transfusion of two or more units of blood products
‡ Calculated as the expected costs of bleeding plus drug costs and monitoring costs per patient
§ Calculated as expected savings minus expected costs

Formulary/Source: L. Basskin, PharmD

improvement in the rate of DVT/PE between those who received no drugs and those who used any of the drugs. The incidence of bleeding, however, was statistically greater in all three drug groups compared with that of the nondrug receivers.

I concluded that since there was an increase in drug toxicities with no improvement in efficacy, the obvious answer was to not recommend that any of the drugs be used for this type of surgery and no further analysis need be done. (Note to clinicians who doubt my findings—most published studies that show higher rates of DVT in knee surgery involved knee replacement and were done when early ambulation was discouraged. Most of our hospital's patients had less invasive arthroscopy and few stayed overnight.)

In the analysis of abdominal surgery, the incidence of DVT/PE was significantly lower in patients who received drugs (and specifically lowest in patients who received LMWH) compared with those who received no anticoagulants. However, there was also a statistically significant increase in the incidence of bleeding in drug receivers (i.e., LMWHs = 10%; SQH = 9.52%; warfarin = 6.67%) compared with those who did not receive any anticoagulant (2.94%).

Review the results and make a recommendation. With respect to abdominal surgery, as can be seen in table 4, the alternative with the highest net benefit in my example was LMWH, with a net benefit of $872 per patient versus $753 for warfarin and $813 for SQH. Interestingly, if acquisition cost of the drug alone had been the sole consideration, warfarin would have been selected. If the acquisition cost plus monitoring costs had been the decisive criteria, SQH would have been selected since it is associated with the lowest combined cost.

Based on the findings of the present study, my recommendation was that all patients in our hospital having abdominal surgery should receive at least two preoperative doses of LMWH.

Conduct a sensitivity analysis. It is important to consider how the recommendations would change if the efficacy, toxicity, or drug acquisition costs were to change. In the present study, one would manipulate the percentages of the drugs being compared with LMWH to determine at what percentage of dollar figure the net benefit from an alternative was greater than the net benefit from LMWH. Presentation of these mathematical calculations is beyond the focus of this paper; it is simply important to note that such an analysis needs to be conducted.

CONCLUDING COMMENTS

While the analysis of drugs used in surgery may be more challenging to analyze than in other fields of medicine, a rational strategy is to approach them on a class-by-class basis, concentrating on those indications and drugs common to most surgeries. Use the techniques and *processes* presented in this article and in previous columns to generate your own analysis of surgical drug use, costs, and outcomes. The key to success is to have a solid understanding of the issues related to surgery, and to carefully select the perspective, costs, and definition of both good and bad outcomes to assess.

What to do when your clinical service has been declared "cost-ineffective"

Learning Objectives:

After reading this chapter, one should be able to:

1. Define and explain the importance of each of the following: perspective, outcome, cost and pharmacoeconomic technique.

2. List three alternative actions one could take to avoid having to discontinue a clinical service which has been determined to be "cost-ineffective".

3. For a given service, and from each of two different perspectives, be able to list the criteria by which you would evaluate the ability of the service to meet users' needs.

Dr. Basskin:

Our hospital's P & T Committee has been trying to standardize the way drugs are evaluated for inclusion on clinical pathways. They have been looking at pathways as a method to minimize patient charges in the hopes of winning some managed care contracts by showing that we are a low-cost, quality provider.

At the same time, a P & T Committee member questioned the "cost-effectiveness" of several clinical services that we have provided for years to our hospital's physicians and patients. Specifically, the services being questioned were: (1) lidocaine, warfarin, and heparin monitoring; (2) antibiotic selection and duration review; and (3) discharge counseling regarding take-home medications. Though my clinical team and I have always regarded these services as clinically successful, the relevance, usefulness, and "cost-effectiveness" of these services have never been scientifically calculated. As our clinical group lacked both the analytical skills and time to properly analyze these services, we asked the team responsible for pathway development to evaluate the cost-effectiveness of our clinical services.

Coincidently, also during this time frame, the hospital administration had declared that a 15% reduction in hospital salaries would be required as a result of a declining patient census. The hospital chairman was on record as stating that despite this reduction, improving patient satisfaction was his number one goal.

To our surprise and dismay, the Pathway team decided that all of our services were *cost-ineffective* (i.e., costs exceeded benefits) and recommended that our energies and all future services be focused on activities that would lower patient charges. In their own evaluation of our services, the administration also concluded that our services were *cost-in-effective* and their solution was even worse—they want to eliminate all clinical positions since they didn't believe they contributed to their idea of "improving patient satisfaction."

We are stunned. Physicians and nurses have raved about how our services for years have saved them time, improved drug use, and helped educate patients about proper use of their medications. Assuming that the Pathway team and the administrators "crunched the numbers" correctly, *what went wrong?*

Signed,

"A confused, and soon-to-be-unemployed, clinical coordinator."

In times of decreasing patient admissions, shorter inpatient stays, capitated patient charges, and budget slashing administrators, it is often easy to look at pharmacy labor and drugs as a natural place to cut the budget and save money. That is why the onus is on the department to justify that their service or drug is worthwhile.

This can only be done if you prove that the costs of a drug or service are less than the benefits that result, AND it is more cost-effective than other uses of the funds. The latter point is something we often forget. While we have rationalized the use of funds within one department, another department may be able to prove its service or product is more cost-effective.

The problem encountered by this reader is that the three groups of people involved—the Pathway team, the administrators, and the clinical pharmacists—each have different objectives and outcomes in mind.

When confronted with a such pharmacoeconomic dilemma, my approach would be to first review the study design to determine if the design and techniques used by someone else are valid and relevant to my situation—in this case, to determine if the clinical services being offered were cost-effective. As the study reader or user, if I am to accept the study results and conclusions of others, it is imperative to determine that my needs and objectives are the same as those used in the study, particularly as they relate to the following four essential elements of a pharmacoeconomic study:

- the study's perspective,
- outcome identification and index of accomplishment,
- cost components, and
- pharmacoeconomic model used.

Interested readers should refer to other well written articles on designing and analyzing a pharmacoeconomic study.[1-3]

By examining these four elements in the context of our reader's problem, we may find out why the conclusions reached by both groups were so vastly different from his or her expectations. On the other hand, we may find out that our reader overestimated the "worth" of the team's services. This reader is certainly not the only one who has not evaluated the cost-effectiveness of services offered. Many hospitals have performed services for years without knowing the costs of those services and without measuring outcomes to determine whether the objectives of the services have been met.

Let's go back to the reader's dilemma. Generally, each group with a vested interest in this problem appeared to have the similar goal of improving patient outcomes and care. In reality, there are many differences among the three groups and many different strategies used to reach their conclusions.

ANALYZING ELEMENTS OF A PHARMACOECONOMIC STUDY

To clarify these differences, let's call the two groups that actually conducted the studies the "Pathway group" and the "Administration group," and we'll call the group represented by the reader the "Clinical group." Next, we'll compare each group's treatment of the four essential elements to determine if and how they differed. Even though the Clinical group didn't actually perform a study, we'll consider the types of elements they would have needed to address to conduct such a study. (Table 1 presents a summary of the following discussion.)

Perspective. The study perspective should be that which is most relevant to the user. In our reader's case, the perspective of all three groups was different. The Pathway group was considering costs and benefits from the perspective of the third-party payer (e.g., insurance companies, managed care). The Administration group appears to have a mixed perspective; it wants growth and increased volume for the hospital but wants costs and benefits to be considered from the perspective of the patient. The Clinical group has the mixed perspectives of satisfying physicians, nurses, and patients through its provision of pharmacy services.

Outcome identification and index of accomplishment. Since the purpose of a program is to achieve its objectives, the choice of the outcome to measure, and the tool by which its success is measured (the *index of accomplishment*) is critical.

The groups differ substantially here. The Pathway group is concentrating on length of stay and charges for drugs and labs as its measure of success. The Administration group is mostly concerned with patient satisfaction, though it's unclear what tool is being used to measure this outcome. The Clinical group has two main objectives to measure: its reputation and credibility as evaluated by physicians, nurses, and patients; and positive therapeutic outcomes (cures without adverse drug events or toxicities). However, unlike the Pathway group, duration of stay was not a criteria they employed, and the Clinical group wants to effect treatments that consider both acute illness and long-term health (e.g., prevention of readmissions).

Cost components. (Note to readers: The specifics of the pharmacoeconomic analyses were provided to me but are not presented in this chapter.) I agree that all three groups should collect variable cost data, ignoring the fixed costs that don't change in the short run. However, the Pathway and Clinical groups used tangible costs, while the Administration group considered the

TABLE I   COMPARING THREE COST-EFFECTIVE ANALYSES OF CLINICAL SERVICES

	Pathway group	Administration group	Clinical group
Perspective	Third-party payers	Patients and hospital	Physicians, nurses, and patients
Cost components	Drugs, labs, and length of stay	Pharmacist salaries and drug costs	Pharmacist and nurses salaries; physician costs
Type of costs	Tangible, variable direct	Tangible and intangible, variable direct and indirect	Tangible, variable direct and indirect
Model	Cost-minimization	Effectiveness	Cost-benefit or cost-effectiveness
Outcomes	Shortened patient stay, decreased labs, use of less expensive drugs	Satisfied patients	Satisfied physicians, nurses; improved patient outcomes; appropriate drug therapy
Index of accomplishment	Decreased patient charges for the immediate visit	Increased patient satisfaction scores	Decreased costs of therapy now and in the future, increase long-term positive outcomes of drug therapy

Formulary/Source: L. Basskin, PharmD

intangible patient costs of pain, grief, and suffering. The Administration and Clinical group also included indirect patient care costs, while the Pathway group focused only on costs directed related to patient care.

Pharmacoeconomic model selected. The Pathway group used a cost-minimization approach: select the option that has the lowest costs. The Administration group apparently used a "simple effectiveness" comparison: select the option that generates the best outcome. The Clinical group, were they to conduct their own study, would have needed to use either a cost-effectiveness or cost benefit analysis approach.

IS SERVICE APPROPRIATE AND COST EFFECTIVE?

Now that we've discussed how treatment of the essential elements of a pharmacoeconomic evaluation differ among the three groups, it is easy to see why their results and conclusions differed. Knowing this information, though, still doesn't solve our reader's problem of proving that his staff should be retained because the services they offer are necessary and cost effective.

What should this reader do? Several solutions could be entertained: change the focus and objectives of the services to meet the needs of others; change the services being offered; or try to show that the existing services do meet the stated objectives of others. It is important to note that the first option actually requires a change in the objectives or focus of the services, while the third option only requires a change in measurement tools. Another option—having administrators change their objectives to meet the ones the Clinical group is already meeting—won't be considered since this rarely happens in real world practice.

Whatever option is selected, the reader will need a plan to get there and a measurement tool that can be used to show that the appropriate outcome is being reached and in a cost-effective manner.

1) Change the focus and goals of the service to meet the objectives of others.

As discussed, the goals of the Clinical group, while admirable, are incongruent with those of the other two groups. If the main objectives and priorities of the hospital are patient satisfaction and reducing patient charges, how can each of the services be modified to meet these goals? Possibilities for each of the existing services include the following:

For the drug level and dosing service, show (i.e., quantify) how this activity can be used to reduce patient charges. Instead of concentrating on trying to make as many dose measurements and adjustments as possible, efforts could be concentrated on trying to reach the therapeutic drug levels as soon as possible to aim for an earlier discharge date. Alternatively, the focus of the service could be on educating nurses and physicians about avoiding unnecessary labs and how to anticipate the need for, and then make, dosing adjustments.

In terms of antibiotic review, there are many ways to make the goals of your service consistent with that of the the Pathway group. Try to select the most cost-effective drug, not just the most effective or the one with the broadest spectrum of activity. Look for ways to reduce costs by earlier changes from IV to oral antibiotics, which should result in earlier discharges. Are automatic stop orders for prophylactic antibiotic regimens in place? Are unnecessary lab or culture tests taking place? Are antibiotic orders reviewed for cost-effective selection? Does patient satisfaction increase when patients recover from acute infection earlier or are discharged earlier? Addressing these questions (either quantifying the results if such initiatives are in place or beginning efforts in these areas) may help reduce costs or help justify this service's continued existence.

With regard to discharge counseling, it may be difficult to show that this service will reduce patient charges. Traditionally, the goal of counseling is to avoid future readmissions due to drug toxicities and to help ensure compliance with medication regimens. Perhaps patient charges could be reduced if reviews were made of their home medications upon admission. One could discontinue certain medications not needed or which are redundant to those given as an inpatient or have the patient bring in their own expensive, nonformulary medications.

The goal of improving patient satisfaction could be met if the success of counseling could be evaluated through patient surveys and compared with patient satisfaction surveys from other areas in the institution. If pharmacist counseling provides the same or better patient satisfaction scores at a lower cost than alternatives, it might be the recommended service.

2) Change the services being offered.

If the objectives of the existing services can't be modified, then more cost-effective services should be considered. As discussed, the primary goal of providing the reader's clinical services appears to be to please other health care professionals (physicians and nurses) while avoiding long-term complications associated with incorrect drug therapy. Unfortunately, this particular therapeutic objective is not as high a priority to the other groups in the hospital at this time. Are there other services that might be better suited to meet the administrators' needs?

For example, for meeting the goal of patient satisfaction, services that require and result in positive direct patient interactions, such as pain management, might be preferable. Or, consider a service such as a pharmacy-run anticoagulation or hypertension clinic that has the potential to reduce the number of physician visits or lab tests.

To fulfill top management's goal of improving patient satisfaction, one solution would be to conduct a patient survey to determine which aspects of hospital care are most important and which could be improved. Our reader then could determine if the clinical team could meet those needs.

3) Use pharmacoeconomic analysis to prove that the Clinical group's plan really does meet the long-term goals of management.

Let's look at objectives of each group. Goals of the Pathway group are very short-term—get patients discharged quickly and inexpensively, and thereby gain patients from managed care groups that use patient charge and cost information as the basis for awarding contracts. The Administration group wants patient satisfaction increased knowing that long-term growth occurs when patients are satisfied. The goals of the Clinical group are generally "long-term" for the patient (e.g., preventing readmissions due to noncompliance or drug toxicity, ensuring that the patient is cured before discharge).

The common feature of both the Administration and Pathway groups is that their focus is on building a patient base. Therefore, the plan for the Clinical group should be to prove, through the use of pharmacoeconomic analyses and outcomes measurements, that the existing services will help management meet these goals.

Questions that need to be answered in such analyses include the following:

■ In what ways will each of the clinical services meet the goal of growth from the perspective of the hospital?

■ What specific outcomes of the existing service that are consistent with a growth philosophy can be measured?

■ What is a valid, reliable, and relevant "index of accomplishment" by which the achievement of each objective can be measured?

■ How many interventions are occurring with each service, and what are the total benefits (how many patients met the index of accomplishment)?

■ What are the direct and indirect variable costs per patient of providing that service?

■ What is the net benefit (benefits minus costs) or the cost-effectiveness ratio (CER; costs divided by nondollar measure of effectiveness)?

■ How does the net benefit or CER compare with the same performance measurements of other departments within the institution? If a high net benefit or CER can be shown, then the current staffing for the Clinical group will probably be maintained since they will have shown that they meet the goals of management in a cost-effective manner, especially in relation to other alternatives.

Of course, there's no guarantee that the services will prove to be cost effective. However, in performing this exercise, you may find ways you could either decrease the costs by being more selective in terms of targeting patients to receive a service, change the objectives of your service, or even find out that there are more cost-effective services that you might offer.

In conclusion, my advice to this reader is to not panic. I believe that the criteria by which the services were evaluated weren't necessarily appropriate and weren't an accurate depiction of what this reader and his or her team has to offer. In this case, the reader either should change the services' goals to be more congruent with the goals of top management, or conduct an analysis to show how the service *can* meet the goals of management.

What this reader *cannot* continue to do is "blindly" carry on, being satisfied that at least the service has met "its own goals" without regard to costs and the needs of the people who pay the team's salary. To do so might result in losing the clinicians most needed to accomplish the service's goals!

REFERENCES

1. Jolicoeur LM, Jones-Grizzle AJ, Boyer JG, et al. "Guidelines for performing a pharmacoeconomic analysis." Am J Hosp Pharm 1992;49:1741-7.
2. Udvarhelyi S, Colditza GA, Rai A, et al. "Cost effectiveness and cost benefit analyses in the medical literature." Ann Intern Med 1992;116:238-244.
3. Milne RJ. "Evaluation of the pharmacoeconomic literature." Pharmacoeconomics 1994;6:337-45.

Using value analysis to select drugs for the formulary from among similar agents

Learning Objectives:

After reading this chapter, one should be able to:

1. Define value analysis and explain why it is useful in evaluating alternatives with multiple outcomes.

2. For a given therapeutic category of drugs, list and "weight" each of the different outcomes one hopes to achieve .

3. Use value analysis to evaluate alternative medications for use in a given therapeutic category or class of agents.

One of the most important uses of pharmacoeconomic analyses by decision makers is to determine which drugs should be made available on the formulary. Though the method of drug selection varies from institution to institution, most agree with the general principle that the drugs ultimately selected should be those that are effective and necessary. However, if a less expensive drug can accomplish the same therapeutic objectives, the less expensive drug should be selected.

I agree with this concept in theory, but there are a number of problems applying such a simple concept in practice. For example, from whose perspective is the drug cost being evaluated, the institution's or the patient's? Often, a drug that costs pennies per dose to the hospital can be quite expensive to the patient when purchased in the outpatient setting.

Another problem is how does one decide if one drug is more or less effective than another if it has several therapeutic uses? For example, beta blockers are used for treating both hypertension and angina. What if an agent is superior for one purpose but inferior for another?

Additionally, there are other important attributes that should be considered in the measurement of a drug's usefulness. These include such factors as:

- the number of FDA indications,
- number and type of contraindications,
- usefulness for patients with allergies to similar drugs,
- bioavailability issues,
- spectrum of activity,
- method of elimination from the body (eg, hepatic, renal),
- drug interactions with food,
- the need for laboratory monitoring,
- onset of action,
- time to steady state,
- safety in pregnancy,

TABLE 1 INPATIENT AND OUTPATIENT COSTS OF THREE CORTICOSTEROID INHALERS

Inhaler	Hospital cost	Outpatient cost
A	$0.01	$32.00
B	$3.00	$16.00
C	$10.00	$11.00

Formulary/Source: L. Basskin, PharmD

- ability to treat other concurrent disease states,
- availability of alternative dosage forms, and
- patient compliance factors (e.g., duration of therapy, frequency of dosing, taste, palatability, and side effect profile).

With so many factors to consider, plus the growth in sheer number of agents within a given class of drugs and more complex marketing and advertising by pharmaceutical manufacturers, it is no wonder that the formulary decision-making process is becoming increasingly complicated. Even the decision-making tools we've learned about in previous columns do not easily assist in finding solutions if more than one factor must be compared simultaneously.

In this chapter, we'll examine some of the shortcomings of cost-minimization analysis (CMA) and cost-effectiveness analysis (CEA) when facing some real world dilemmas in which multiple factors should be considered. Lastly, I'll introduce a new model I've developed that allows one to assess multiple drug-related issues simultaneously in order to make a sound formulary decision.

SHORTCOMINGS OF COST MINIMIZATION AND COST-EFFECTIVENESS ANALYSES

In general, we know that if more than one drug is equally effective, CMA can be used to determine the most cost-effective agent to add to the formulary. The drug with the lowest combined acquisition and administration cost is selected.

While this approach is fine if we only have one perspective in mind—that of the hospital—how would we assess more than one perspective. For example, table 1 presents actual 1996 costs of three corticosteroid inhalers at a community hospital (part of a large buying group). We'll assume that all are equally effective and that there is no difference in patient compliance between any of the agents.

From the hospital perspective, the temptation is to select inhaler A. This inhaler is practically free to the hospital, yet costs the patient $32.00 when purchased in the outpatient setting. Inhaler B costs $3.00 in the inpatient setting and $16.00 when purchased in the outpatient setting—which is half the outpatient cost of inhaler A. The inpatient and outpatient costs for inhaler C are nearly the same, but they are quite a bit higher than what the hospital would pay for inhaler A or B.

How should the P & T Committee decide which inhaler to select? Is it the

		% reduction	
	Yearly	**in total**	**Cost-effectiveness**
Drug	**cost**	**cholesterol**	**ratio**
Happystatin	$300	30%	$10.00
Sluggishstatin	$480	40%	$12.00
Fatinstatin	$600	45%	$13.33
Wastastatin	$750	25%	$30.00

TABLE 2 ECONOMIC COMPARISON OF FOUR FICTITIOUS HMG-COA REDUCTASE INHIBITORS

* Dollars per percentage point reduction

Formulary/Source: L. Basskin, PharmD

P & T Committee's role to consider the outpatient cost of drugs in its inpatient drug selection process? Would it matter if the patient had insurance that paid for the inhaler? Would it matter if the price so discouraged patients from purchasing the inhaler that they became noncompliant and may soon be seen in the emergency room because of an acute asthmatic attack? Does it matter that the institution may use only a small number of inhalers per patient in the inpatient setting to address short-term, acute needs, while each individual patients may require 12 to 24 inhalers per year as outpatients? If we are to address these questions, a decision-making tool other than CMA needs to be used.

To present another example, we know that CEA is the best approach to use when comparing drugs that differ in "primary" measures of effectiveness (e.g., number of cures, decrease in blood pressure units, drop in units of cholesterol). Table 2 shows the cost of three fictitious HMG-CoA reductase inhibitors (hospital perspective) and the expected percentage decline in total cholesterol.

Which agent should be selected for the formulary? We can forget about wastastatin since it is the most expensive and least effective. Happystatin has the lowest cost-effectiveness ratio (CER) at $10.00, but with a 30% reduction in cholesterol, is less effective than sluggishstatin and fatinstatin. Is it worth paying the higher cost to gain more effectiveness?

The answer depends on both how much extra the hospital has to pay, and whether the benefits of extra reductions in cholesterol are clinically significant. We have to calculate the difference in CERs, defined as the difference in cost ÷ difference in efficacy, by comparing the two drugs with higher CERs with happystatin.

For sluggishstatin, this works out to $1,800/year/point reduction [($480 minus $300) ÷ (0.4 minus 0.3)]. For fatinstatin, the difference is $2,000/ year/point reduction [($600 minus $300) ÷ (0.45 minus 0.3)]. If patients were to take these drugs for 20 years, the cost difference would be $36,000 and $40,000, respectively, for each percentage point reduction. Is the extra reduction in cholesterol levels worth the additional expense? What about the difference in morbidity and mortality between these three drugs, or the ability of one to

TABLE 3 VALUE SCORES FOR THREE CALCIUM CHANNEL BLOCKERS*

Primary measures	Drug A	Drug B	Drug C
Hypertension	4	4	3
Angina	4	2	2
CHF	4	2	1
Arrhythmias	2	2	4
Secondary measures			
Institution cost	2	3	4
No. of FDA indications	4	3	2
Contraindications	4	3	2
Elimination pathways	3	1	2
Drug interactions	3	3	4
Alternative dosage forms	1	3	4
Onset	4	4	3
Compliance-related measures			
Duration of therapy	2	2	2
Taste/Palatability	3	4	4
Patient cost	1	3	4
Side effect profile	4	3	2
Dosing frequency	4	3	1

* Each measure of value is ranked from 0 to 4, where 0 = of no value, 1 = limited or infrequent value, 2 = average value, 3 = generally valuable, and 4 = highest value or utility to the institution. Rankings were based on a review of the scientific literature in which these parameters were evaluated for each drug.

Formulary/Source: L. Basskin, PharmD

prevent the occurrence on a myocardial infarction, or to reverse coronary artery disease?

There is at least one more important issue that needs to be addressed in the formulary decision-making process. As stated previously, the shortcoming of CMA and CEA is that they require that the drugs differ in only one measure of effectiveness, which is rarely the case. In addition, what about all of the other factors discussed earlier that make a drug more valuable, such as number of FDA approved indications, routes of elimination, and patient compliance factors?

Unlike CMA and CEA, a method that *does* assess multiple measures of effectiveness is cost-benefit analysis. In this type of analysis, all of the benefits are subtracted from the costs of therapy, and the drug with the highest net benefits is selected. However, the shortcoming with this approach is the extreme difficulty in assigning a dollar value to each of the different effectiveness variables.

Rather than continue to struggle with these existing models and their deficiencies, I'm going to describe a new model I've developed that compares the usefulness or "utility" of the drugs to each other so that the most *valuable*

	Weighting of importance	Drug A	Drug B	Drug C
TABLE 4 WEIGHTING OF THE VALUE SCORES FOR THREE CALCIUM CHANNEL BLOCKERS*				
Primary measures				
Hypertension	10	40	40	30
Angina	10	40	20	20
CHF	8	32	16	8
Arrhythmias	7	14	14	28
Secondary measures				
Institution cost	8	16	24	32
No. of FDA indications	5	20	15	10
Contraindications	7	28	21	14
Elimination pathways	4	12	4	8
Drug interactions	4	12	12	16
Alternative dosage forms	3	3	9	12
Onset	2	8	8	6
Compliance-related measures				
Duration of therapy	4	8	8	8
Taste/Palatability	3	9	12	12
Patient cost	4	4	12	16
Side effect profile	7	28	21	14
Dosing frequency	4	16	12	4
Total value score		**290**	**248**	**238**

* The value scores from table 3 are multiplied by the weighting factor (column 1 of this table) to determine a weighted score for each variable for drugs A, B, and C.

*Formulary/*Source: L. Basskin, PharmD

drug to the institution can be added to the formulary.

NEW MODEL: ASSESSING MULTIPLE VARIABLES OF EFFECTIVENESS

In this new model, I developed a technique I call *value analysis.* Unlike the other more traditional pharmacoeconomic models in which drug cost is divided by a measure of effectiveness, this model assumes that the value of each drug is related to its usefulness or utility, and it can be scored or evaluated on that basis.

Since this technique is being used to make a formulary decision, my method of maximizing value to the institution is to select the drug that provides the most utility for the greatest number of patients. I realize there will always be a need for drugs that meet certain niches for a limited number of patients, but most formulary decisions are based on what benefits the mass population of patients.

The overall objective of my model is to list, rank, and compare all of the different aspects about a drug that make it more valuable to the patient population at my institution. The drug's cost is then just one more component of value.

What makes my model unique compared with others is that I can consider both the institution's and the patient's costs and other drug-related concerns at the same time. The steps to conduct this type of analysis are as follows:

1. Identify the drugs under consideration for formulary inclusion that accomplish a similar purpose, or are of the same chemical class (eg, antibiotics, beta blockers, ACE-inhibitors, calcium channel blockers, HMG-CoA reductase inhibitors, alpha blockers, benzodiazepines, oral sulfonylureas.)

2. List all of the measures by which the value of a drug will be gauged. These include traditional measures of effectiveness such as cure and number of lives saved; secondary measures of value to the institution such as costs, associated adverse events, toxicities, and administration issues; and compliance-related factors.

3. Perform a literature search for each of the drugs under consideration, and use the information gained to rank each drug for each parameter being evaluated. I use a 0 to 4 ranking system, where 0 = provides no value to 4 = provides maximum available value (see table 3).

4. Multiply the value scores times a weighting factor from 1 to 10 to reflect the relative importance of that parameter to other parameters (see table 4).

For example, I may rate "curative properties" as a 10, but palatability or taste as a 2. My rating factor depends on how important I think the usefulness of that parameter is to requirements of the drug as it will be administered in my setting and from my perspective. It's also a function of what other formulary agents are available that can accomplish the same purpose.

In my model, I can consider both patient and institutional drug costs and can weight them equally or disproportionately, depending on the importance I want to assign to each. This ranking and weighting is subjective, but it allows me flexibility in varying the rankings and weightings and seeing how the results might change.

5. Add up the weighted score for each drug to obtain an effectiveness score.

Tables 3 and 4 show an example I've worked through for three calcium channel blockers under consideration at my institution, where the goal was to include only one of them on the formulary. Table 3 shows the raw ranking scores of value from 0 to 4. Table 4 shows the weighting factors applied based on the importance at my institution (column 1), and the total weighted value scores for each drug.

According to the results, drug A has the highest value (290 points) compared with drug B (248) or drug C (238). Assuming that neither drugs B nor C would be required because they meet some unusual or specific patient niche, Drug A would be selected for the formulary.

CONCLUDING COMMENTS

In this chapter, I pointed out some of the problems and considerations associated with using pharmacoeconomic analysis to select drugs from within a class for formulary inclusion. I introduced a new model that allows one to consider many measures of value or utility of a drug to a specific institution. While some readers may feel uncomfortable with the idea of selecting a drug based on a "points system," this is simply a method for incorporating the many features of drugs—other than the usual measures of primary effectiveness and cost—that should be considered in the formulary decision-making process.

By using spreadsheet software, any user can determine how the relative rankings change if any one of the parameters were to change (e.g., new FDA indication, new dosage form, substantial price change of any one drug).

Discounting in pharmacoeconomic analyses: when and how to do it

Learning Objectives:
After reading this chapter, one should be able to:

1. Explain the rationale for discounting future payments and receipts.

2. Calculate the present value of a future lump sum or stream of payments, given the discount rate, number of time periods, and the future or face value.

3. Utilize discounting in a therapeutic problem in which future annual or lump sum payments are required.

When performing pharmacoeconomic analysis, we try to measure whenever possible, the results in either dollars or dollars per "unit of effectiveness" (i.e., cost per life saved). For example, in cost-benefit analysis, we select the alternative that generates the highest amount of net benefits in dollars (benefits less costs). Ordinarily, by choosing dollars as our sole unit of measurement, we avoid the problem of comparing "apples with oranges." However, if the costs that must be paid or received occur in different time periods and the number of years between dollars paid or received is large, the dollars need to be converted into a common denominator—today's dollars. This chapter will discuss the why, when, and how of the use of discounting in the context of performing pharmacoeconomic evaluations.

RATIONALE FOR DISCOUNTING

The reason for converting future dollars into today's dollars is based on the assumption that a dollar in the future is worth less than a dollar today. One rationale for this assumption is that the costs of goods or services will continue to rise in the future due to inflation. To explain this concept in another way, if the value of a dollar is based on the quantity of goods or services that can be exchanged for it, then a dollar in the future is worth less than a dollar today because future dollars have less buying power (assuming inflation causes prices to rise).

Let's assume that except for total out of pocket costs, you have no preference if goods or services are purchased today or in the future. However, you would probably like to hang on to your dollars of today and not spend them until you have to. We need a method of calculating how much less it would cost you today for those services compared with waiting to pay for them at a future date. That method is known as discounting.

One way to think of why you need to discount future payments might be to consider a more personal example. Let's say you are offered the chance to

Definition of terms used in discounting

Discount rate: The interest rate used to determine the present value of future payments. It is based on the user's rate of borrowing or investing. The typical range is 5% to 10%.

Present value: The value, in today's dollars, of lump sum and annuity payments in the future. The amount will always be less than the face amount of the future value, since, during inflationary times, it costs less today to buy the goods and services compared with buying them in the future.

Future value: The face amount, in future dollars, or the actual projected cost of a future expenditure. It needs to be converted into present value (today's dollars) when comparing it with payments made at other dates.

Lump sum: A one-time payment to be made on a specific date, now or in the future.

Annuity: A series or stream of equal, periodic payments. In pharmacoeconomic analysis, this usually consists of equal annual payments. The annuity may begin now or in the future.

New present value: The value obtained by summing up all the individual present values, in today's dollars, of relevant annuities and lump sums.

prepurchase your cemetery plot today for $10,000, but you won't need it (you hope) for 25 more years. In trying to evaluate whether the $10,000 is a fair price, you are told that 25 years from now, the same plot will cost $25,000.

Discounting is a mathematical tool that allows you to determine how much you would have to invest today at a certain rate of compound interest to earn $25,000 25 years from now. If that amount is less than $10,000, you would be better off investing the amount and letting it grow in value to reach the $25,000, rather than paying the $10,000 today. Of course, you may choose to pay a premium today just to make sure there's a home for you in the future. Discounting helps you with the math of decision-making only. It neither alters the supply of goods and services nor replaces personal preferences about wanting something pleasant now or wanting to put off something unpleasant for as long as possible.

DISCOUNTING: THE MATH

Discounting is the method by which the cash outlays and inflows (costs and benefits) of the future are converted or discounted into "present value" dollars of today. Information you'll need to know to conduct discounting are the discount rate, the number of years until the future payment, and the future value.

Also, you'll need to understand that there are two kinds of payments used in discounting—these are generally referred to as lump sums and annuities. (These and other common terms used in discounting are defined in Exhibit 1.) Determination of the present value of a lump sum can either be performed on

TABLE 1	PRESENT VALUE OF A DOLLAR			
No. of years	Discount rate			
	2%	5%	10%	20%
1	0.98	0.953	0.909	0.833
2	0.961	0.907	0.826	0.694
3	0.942	0.864	0.751	0.578
4	0.924	0.823	0.683	0.482
5	0.906	0.783	0.621	0.401
6	0.888	0.746	0.564	0.334
7	0.871	0.711	0.513	0.279
8	0.853	0.676	0.466	0.232
9	0.836	0.644	0.424	0.193
10	0.821	0.614	0.385	0.161
15	0.743	0.481	0.239	0.065
20	0.673	0.377	0.148	0.026

*Formulary/*Source: Dewhurst RFJ. Business cost-benefit analysis. New York: McGraw-Hill, 1972:277.

a calculator or obtained from a table, such as table 1, which can be found in any finance book.

The formula for determining the present value of a payment to be made in the future is:

$$PV = FV \div (1+i)^n$$

In this formula, PV stands for present value; FV equals future value; "i" stands for interest rate; and "n" equals number of years. For example, using a discount rate of 10% and a future value (2 years from now) of $100, the present value is $82.64 $(1 + 0.1 = 1.1; 1.1^2 = 1.21;$ $100 divided by 1.21 = $82.64).

Alternatively, you can determine the multiplicand by referring to table 1. The multiplicand is found at the intersection of the number of years column (in our example, 2 years) and the discount rate column (in our example, 10%). Thus, in our example, the multiplicand for a sum of money at an interest rate of 10% 2 years from the present time is 0.826. Multiply the future dollar amount by this factor to obtain the discounted present value (in our example, $100 x 0.826 = $82.60).

The simplest method to determine the present value of an annuity is to refer to table 2. Multiply the annual payment times the multiplicand. For example, if $100 is to be paid annually for 3 years, using a discount rate of 20%, the multiplicand from table 2 is 2.527. The present value of $100 3 years from now considering a discount rate of 20% would be $252.70 (i.e., $100 x 2.527).

To be certain that you've done the math correctly, the present value should always be less than the future value amount. For example, the face value of the annuity in the previous example would be $300 ($100 times 3 years), which is more than the present value of $252.70.

TABLE 2   PRESENT VALUE OF AN ANNUITY

No. of years	Discount rate			
	2%	5%	10%	20%
1	1	1	1	1
2	1.98	1.953	1.909	1.833
3	2.941	2.86	2.735	2.527
4	3.883	3.724	3.486	3.105
5	4.807	4.547	4.169	3.587
6	5.713	5.33	4.79	3.988
7	6.601	6.076	5.354	4.322
8	7.472	6.787	5.867	4.601
9	8.325	7.463	6.333	4.833
10	9.161	8.107	6.757	5.026
15	13.026	10.763	8.216	5.509
20	16.526	12.843	9.12	5.702

*Formulary/*Source: Dewhurst RFJ. Business cost-benefit analysis. In: New York: McGraw-Hill, 1972;278.

A slightly more complicated calculation is required when an annuity begins in the future. In this case, two steps are involved. First, determine the present value of the annuity back to the year in which it began. Next, treat the present value of the annuity like a lump sum future value and discount it back to today's dollars.

As an example, suppose you were offered a choice between receiving a $500 annuity that begins 5 years from now and continues for 10 years or a lump sum amount today that could be invested at a rate of 5%. The face value of the annuity is $5,000 ($500 times 10 years), but it is worth less than this in today's dollars. Step 1: The present value of the annuity beginning 5 years from now would be $4,053 ($500 times 8.107 [from table 2: 5%, 10 years]). Step 2: Using table 1, the 5% factor for a lump sum received 5 years from now is 0.783. Therefore the present value of the annuity is $3,173 ($4,053 times 0.783 [from table 1: 5%, 5 years]). Thus, if offered a choice, you would have no preference between receiving $3,173 today or $500 per year for 10 years beginning 5 years from now.

SELECTING THE DISCOUNT RATE

What discount rate should you select when conducting a pharmacoeconomic analysis to make a decision between two or more alternatives? Unfortunately, there is no set rule. Some pharmacoeconomists may use the rate of inflation, the average or highest rate of interest at which the institution has to borrow money, or the rate of return required for an investment. Choose the rate that is most relevant to the user. My personal preference when conducting an analysis for an institution is to use the average cost of borrowing, since the institution often has borrowed money to finance the purchase of inventory or new equipment.

TABLE 3	**HOW TO DETERMINE IF DISCOUNTING IS NECESSARY***			
Sensitivity ratio[†]	**Discount rate**			
	2%	**5%**	**10%**	**20%**
1.25	12	4.8	2.4	1.2
1.5	22	8.8	4.4	2.2
1.75	30	12	6	3
2	36	14.4	7.2	3.6

* If the number of years between the first and last payment among alternatives is greater than the number identified in the boxed section of this table—at the intersection point of the selected sensitivity ratio and discount rate—then discounting should be performed.

† = arbitrarily selected ratios (FV ÷ PV) that allows one to consider different breakpoints at which the differences between discounted and face value amounts may result in a significant impact.

Formulary/Source: L. Basskin, PharmD

Keep in mind that as the rate of interest used for discounting increases, the net present value of the amount becomes lower. To make this concept easier to understand, think about it from an investment perspective. When interest rates are higher, it takes less money invested today to earn the same dollar amount in the future.

One may ask if there is a simple method to determine when to discount future cash flow. Or, another way to phrase this: is there an easy way to tell if results obtained with use of "face value" amounts will differ significantly from the results obtained when discounting is used? I've attempted to simplify this decision with a chart I've created, table 3. The numbers in this table represent the minimum number of years necessary between first and last payments for discounting to have a significant impact.

To use this table, locate the intersection point between the selected discount rate (column 2 through 5) and the sensitivity ratio (defined as FV ÷ PV) you wish to consider (column 1). The sensitivity ratios I have considered range from 1.25 to 2.0 (ratios shown in column 1 of the table). If the number of years between the first and last payment between any two alternatives is greater than the number of years shown at the relevant intersection point in table 3, then discounting could produce a significant result.

For example, if you want to detect a 50% difference in the effect of discounting (FV ÷ PV = 1.5) when using a 10% discount rate, then the relevant number is 4.4 years. If the number of years between the earliest payment with one alternative and the latest payment with another alternative is more than 4.4 years, then discounting should be performed. As a general rule, the longer the number of years between payments, and the higher the discount rate, the more likely that discounting will result in a significant difference.

One other factor to keep in mind is that it is impossible to state how much of a "result" between a discounted amount and a nondiscounted amount

TABLE 4	**ALTERNATIVE TREATMENTS FOR ACUTE MYOCARDIAL INFARCTION**			
	PTCA + stent now	Drugs for 5 years then PTCA	Drugs for 10 years then CABG	Thrombolytic now + drugs for 7 years
1996 costs	$7,300	$300	$0	$2,500
Present value factor	1	1	1	1
Present value	$7,300	$300	$0	$2,500
Annual drug costs	$0	$800	$800	$800
Present value factor (from table 2)	N/A	4.169	6.757	5.354
Present value	$0	$3,335	$5,406	$4,283
Surgery	$0	$4,500	$8,000	$0
Present value factor (from table 1)	N/A	0.621	0.385	N/A
Present value	$0	$2,795	$3,080	$0
Net present value using 10% discount rate	$7,300	$6,130	$8,486	$6,783

Formulary/Source: L. Basskin, PharmD

would be considered "significant" for all users. For instance, in situations when alternatives have similar face values, a "small" difference could be viewed as being very important.

SAMPLE PROBLEM

Let's try a problem you might encounter in a health care setting in which a decision must be made between alternatives and in which the costs must be incurred in different years. Take the example of a person admitted with an acute myocardial infarction. Your cardiologists are considering four different options. (The source of the following data was from a review of the medical literature and a retrospective review of patient charts and medical records, and billing records. This study was done from the perspective of the patient, so patient charges and drug costs were used in the analysis). For simplicity sake, let's assume all four options have an equal rate of efficacy at prolonging life. The four options are to:

1. Perform percutaneous transluminal coronary angioplasty (PTCA) today and place a stent. The cost today is $7,300, and no further drug therapy would be required.

2. Give drug therapy for the next 5 years at $800 per year, and then perform PTCA at a cost of $4,500. Lab costs of $300 would be required in the current year.

3. Give the patient 10 years of drug therapy at $800 per year and then perform coronary artery bypass surgery (CABG) at a cost of $8,000.

TABLE 5	**SENSITIVITY ANALYSIS OF NET PRESENT VALUE USING DIFFERENT DISCOUNT RATES**			
	PTCA + stent now	Drugs for 5 years then PTCA	Drugs for 10 years then CABG	Thrombolytic now + drugs for 7 years
Face value for comparative purposes	$7,300	$8,800	$16,000	$8,100
Net present value at 5% discount rate	$7,300	$7,461	$11,398	$7,361
Net present value at 10% discount rate	$7,300	$6,430	$8,486	$6,783
Net present value at 20% discount rate	$7,300	$4,974	$5,309	$5,958

Formulary/Source: L. Basskin, PharmD

4. Give thrombolytic therapy (e.g., t-PA or streptokinase) at a cost of $2,500 in the current year followed by an average of 7 more years of drug therapy at $800 per year.

This example has been simplified by not allowing the annual drug costs to increase from year to year, and by limiting the analysis to 10 years. These assumptions could be varied using spreadsheet software.

Before proceding with the example, let's use table 3 to determine if we should perform discounting. Suppose we decide that we want to perform discounting only if the future value is at least one and one-half times the net present value. Using a discount rate of 10% (the discount rate that we will use in the following example) and a sensitivity ratio of 1.5 (see table 3), the intersection point is 4.4 years. Since the greatest number of years between the first and last payments among alternatives is 10 years (for the alternative of drugs for 10 years then CABG in the following example), and 10 years is greater than the 4.4 years shown in table 3, discounting should be performed.

Once the decision has been made to perform discounting, we need to determine the net present value of each alternative. To do this, you'll need to take each lump sum and use table 1 to discount those amounts and use table 2 (present value of an annuity) to discount annuity type payments (i.e., annual drug costs). The net present value is the sum of all of those amounts in today's dollars. Table 4 shows the results of the analysis using a 10% discount rate, which is the cost of borrowing money to the patient.

Let's work through one of the alternatives—drugs for 5 years then PTCA. Because the $300 laboratory costs are to be paid this year (PV = FV), a factor of 1.0 is used. The annual drug costs of $800 represent a 5-year annuity, which, at a 10% discount rate are translated using the factor 4.169 (from table 2). The present value of the annuity is $3,335 ($800 times 4.169). The present value of the lump sum payment of the future surgery is $2,795 ($4,500 times 0.621 [from table 1]). Finally, the net present value, or the total of the present values of all payments, is $6,130 ($300 + $3,335 + $2,795).

Comparing all options, the alternative with the lowest net present value is PTCA in 5 years. This is the alternative that would be most cost-effective using cost-minimization analysis and a discount rate of 10%.

Table 5 shows the results of the sensitivity analysis performed to determine if the most cost-effective alternative would change if one or more of the variables changed. In this case, discount rates were varied. When the face value (i.e., no discounting) is examined, immediate PTCA and stent is least expensive, followed by thrombolytics, PTCA in 5 years, and CABG. At a discount rate of 5% no change in order of preference is seen. However, discounting at 10% does change the order of preference: delayed PTCA now ranks first followed by thrombolytics, PTCA and stent, and CABG. As we increase the discount rate, paying dollars in the future becomes less important, since those dollars are worth less today. At a discount rate of 20%, the order has changed substantially. Delayed PTCA is still first, but CABG now ranks second, followed by thrombolytic therapy and PTCA and stent today. You can see that the choice of an appropriate discount rate can substantially change the relative rankings of alternatives.

CONCLUDING COMMENTS

In this chapter, I've showed the importance of discounting—a technique to be used when costs and benefits occur in different time periods—and presented how to use the technique to convert future outlays and inflows into a common unit: dollars of today. I also showed you how to perform a simple calculation with alternatives and the importance of the discount rate selection. The next time you have to compare the costs of life-long therapy versus immediate surgery, don't forget to discount the future cash stream or lump sum payments, as it may completely change your recommendation.

Keep in mind, however, that discounting has its own inherent difficulties, such as selecting the time frame over which costs will be measured and, if you don't assume equal efficacy, the need to value and discount future benefits or consider different outcomes. In addition, while you can determine the net present value of an alternative, this technique won't tell you if the price is a reasonable one to avoid an outcome such as premature death or improve the quality of life. However, these questions would need to be answered regardless of type of analysis chosen and despite application or lack of application of a discount rate.

How to evaluate different clinical interventions for ensuring the selection of appropriate antibiotics

Learning Objectives:

After reading this chapter, one should be able to:

1. Define "confounding variables" and list three methods by which a negative impact on study design could be minimized.

2. List different interventions designed to improve outcomes from antibiotic use, and evaluate the ability of each intervention at achieving the desired outcome.

3. Determine the average cost of healthcare resources used to accomplish each intervention, and select from among alternative interventions using cost-minimization analysis.

Dear Dr. Basskin,

I am a clinical pharmacist with an HMO in California. We believe we have a problem with the use of certain antibiotics within our institution. Specifically, the use of expensive third-generation cephalosporins has been increasing on a monthly basis. Based on a review of a sample of culture and sensitivity reports, it seems these drugs are being used when less expensive drugs, such as the first-generation cephalosporins, would suffice. In addition, because of the relatively poor coverage of the third-generation cephalosporins for infections caused by bacteria other than gram negative aerobic organisms, it seems that quite often, the drug is ineffective and needs to be changed to a drug that provides better coverage.

I don't believe that patients are dying as a result of the inappropriate prescribing. Drug therapy that does not result in a cure, eventually does get changed to one that does. However, the patient's recovery is delayed, and the costs to the HMO for an increased stay and unnecessary antibiotic therapy could have been lower if the correct empiric therapy was selected, or a better therapy had been adopted, at an earlier date.

While the infectious disease physician corrects these problems when consulted, the HMO wants to discourage the use of specialist consults. Our Formulary Committee has asked me to suggest a cost-effective intervention that can be made by pharmacists. Based on what I've read and seen elsewhere, I have generated some ideas for interventions. These include restrictions on use, pharmacist review of daily culture and sensitivity reports, and therapeutic substitution. However, I need to be certain that my ultimate recommendation will improve patient outcomes and/or reduce costs to the HMO. How can I design a study to determine if some sort of pharmacist intervention will be beneficial to my HMO? Also, how do I calculate how many FTEs to request to implement such a plan?

Signed,
Dr. Henry B.
Clinical Pharmacist
Texas

It's admirable that our reader wants to study the problem before she implements a plan. Too often, a plan or intervention is implemented before adequate time has been taken to evaluate all costs and benefits.

Antibiotics, as this reader knows first hand, are often the target of interventional efforts because, as a class, they usually represent the largest percentage of an institution's drug budget. What Formulary Committees are chiefly concerned about is the potential misuse and inappropriate use of these products, which, if it occurs, can ultimately drive up antibiotic costs. Specifically, antibiotic costs can increase when:

■ more expensive intravenous formulations are used when less expensive oral forms would have sufficed,

■ more broad-spectrum antibiotics are used when narrower spectrum agents would have sufficed,

■ antibiotic selection is not changed when culture and sensitivity reports indicate that a less expensive agent would be equally effective, and

■ the most cost-effective antibiotics are not selected.

To encourage more appropriate selection and use of antibiotics, any number of interventions are typically tried, e.g., restrictions on drug use, mandatory reviews or consultations from pharmacy or infectious disease specialists, automatic stop orders or conversions from IV to oral antibiotics, automatic therapeutic substitutions, and daily review of culture and sensitivity reports.

The general goal of these interventions is the same—to have the physicians start with, or switch to, an antibiotic likely to cover the suspected organism at the lowest possible cost using the least invasive route. However, these interventions are often implemented without giving sufficient thought to the precise objectives or implementation costs.

PROSPECTIVE STUDY: KEY POINTS

A prospective clinical study is an excellent way of determining which alternative is most cost effective and is the step I would advise our reader to take. First, to ensure that the results will be both useful and valid, a study needs to be appropriately designed. Questions that must be answered include the following:

■ What is the desired goal or objective of the intervention—shorter lengths of stay, improved cure rate without changing drugs, earlier conversion

EXHIBIT 1

Possible confounding variables in a study of infectious diseases

- the specific or multiple infectious disease states of the patient,
- incidence of antibiotic resistance,
- other reasons for infection (e.g., fungal, parasitic, viral),
- duration of antibiotic therapy prior to admission,
- comorbid conditions, such as immunosuppression, malnutrition, diabetes or other diseases that might delay healing,
- concurrent therapy that might impair healing or antibiotic effectiveness such as chemotherapy, corticosteroids, or drugs that interfere with absorption of oral antibiotics.

to oral antibiotics, decreased incidence of antimicrobial resistance?
- How will the desired outcome be measured?
- What are the costs associated with implementing these interventions?
- Which intervention results in the most cost-effective outcomes?

There are several key elements of a prospective study. One key element to pay particular attention to is patient selection. Even the most useful study will only tell you how effective a therapy or intervention will likely be for patients who meet the same criteria as those enrolled in the study. Obviously, there are many patient characteristics not being studied or controlled (called "confounding variables") that might influence the study results. Confounding variables include concurrent disease states; patient age, sex, or weight; and use of concurrent medications. Some confounding variables of a study of infectious disease and antibiotic use are shown in Exhitit 1.

There are two ways to design a study to acknowledge and eliminate the effects of confounding variables. The first is to exclude patients with confounding variables. For instance, we could choose to include only patients who were not taking any drug other than the study drug, had specific or limited number of disease states, had no risk of immunosuppression, and fell within a narrow range for age and weight. Obviously, the problem with this approach is that the results cannot be extrapolated to the typical population of a health care facility.

If we do not wish to exclude large numbers of patients, how do we avoid concluding that the results are due to the confounding variables and not the intervention itself? One solution is to ensure that each group in the study has an equal number of patients with confounding variables. For example, if multiple infectious disease states are a confounding variable, then each group should have the same number of patients with urinary tract infection, pneumonia, etc. This is done by randomizing the patients between the groups and ensuring that the sample size is large enough to allow for an equal distribution of all confounding variables between the two groups. In this way, it is hoped that all groups in the study are an accurate reflection of the typical patients seen in your institution.

Practically, I suggest using a combination of these two options. First, narrow the study population somewhat if the confounding variables are important to exclude or would jeopardize the safety of the study participants. For example, patients with drug allergies or renal failure are often excluded from studies because of the risk to their health at the "normal doses" usually employed in clinical trials. Next, randomize all of the patients eligible for entry between the alternative groups.

ANSWERING OUR READER'S QUESTION

To help our reader solve her problem, I'm going to suggest that she carry out a prospective study of the different ways in which antibiotic use can be improved. While there are many goals of an antibiotic management program, the goal of this study will be to ensure that the therapy with the lowest total cost is selected.

Study assumptions. For this study, I'll assume each antibiotic regimen eventually results in a cure. While this assumption is not always true with the entire patient population, I am going to narrow the population being studied by excluding patients who are sicker due to confounding variables. For example, I'll exclude patients who have a higher than normal risk of not being cured with antibiotics. These include patients with septicemia; those who are immunosuppressed because of AIDS; those receiving chronic corticosteroids or chemotherapy; those with suspected fungal, viral, or parasitic disease; and those likely to be infected with a recurring resistant strain of bacterium. I'll also exclude patients for whom an infectious disease consult has been obtained.

Another reason I've excluded very sick patients is that I believe physicians are reluctant to enroll patients with potentially life-threatening illnesses in a pharmacist-controlled study. Of course, limiting the number of eligible patients will also limit the ability to extrapolate these results to all the patients in an institution.

The study hypothesis is that the cost of therapy for patients who are eventually cured—as measured by the drugs, laboratory tests, and length of stay—can be decreased with the appropriately selected pharmacist intervention. Specific interventions to evaluate are as follows:

1. Daily reviews of culture and sensitivity reports by a clinical pharmacist.

2. Interventions made by pharmacists at the time the drug is ordered, such as automatic stop orders and suggestions for therapeutic interchanges.

3. No intervention. The option of no interaction was included to assess if adoption of either "active" intervention was superior to no action taken. This group is referred to as the "control group."

Two other options I considered, but chose not to evaluate, were restrictions on drug use and physician education. Personally, I'm not fond of restricting the use of a drug because it places the pharmacist in the role of policeman and not a consultant, and it forces confrontation with physicians over drug selection issues. As for physician education, it is difficult to attribute changes in drug therapy to the effects of physican education exclusive of other ongoing interventions being evaluated.

The perspective of this study will be that of the HMO.

TABLE 2	COMPARISON OF TOTAL COSTS OF CULTURE AND SENSITIVITY REPORT REVIEW VERSUS NO INTERVENTION

| | Cost-minimization analysis of different antibiotic programs* | | | |
	Pharmacist review of C & S	No intervention	Savings (cost) per patient	Savings (cost) 10,000 patients
Labs	$100	$125	$25	$250,000
Drugs	$164	$205	$41	$410,000
Physician costs	$126	$183	$57	$570,000
Pharmacist time	$28	$0	($28)	($280,000)
Length of stay	$1,650	$2,090	$440	$4,400,000
Total savings	**$2,068**	**$2,603**	**$535**	**$5,350,000**

* From an HMO perspective

*Formulary/*Source: L. Basskin, PharmD

The model chosen will be cost-minimization analysis. In this model, the complete costs of each alternative are accumulated, and the alternative with the lowest cost is selected. You may recall that one requirement of using this model is that the outcomes of each alternative and the probabilities of occurrence are equal. I'm going to use the assumption of the reader that all patients in her study are eventually cured.

METHODS

The study methods are to select patients who meet the inclusion criteria (i.e., exclude the sicker patients) and randomly assign them to one of the three groups. Since the reader is concerned about cephalosporins, we'll define eligible patients as those who meet the inclusion criteria and for whom the initial drug ordered was one of four third-generation cephalosporins: ceftazidime (Fortaz, Tazicef, Tazidime), ceftizoxime (Cefizox), ceftriaxone (Rocephin), or cefotaxime (Claforan).

Extensive intervention. In this arm of the study, empiric therapy will be allowed as an attempt to take some of the discretion from the physician. Orders for prophylactic antibiotics will be stopped after 3 days unless the physician intervenes on the third day and extends the therapeutic course. When appropriate, a more narrow spectrum, less expensive antibiotic will be recommended for empiric therapy. In addition, if coverage for a suspected pathogenic organism was omitted (e.g., for anaerobic coverage) or for a suspected organism not covered by the antibiotics orders (e.g., *Streptococcus pneumoniae* for a community acquired pneumonia), then a different drug will be recommended.

This intervention is deemed "extensive" since it is very time intensive. In addition to the time required to train pharmacists and review the therapy and chart of each patient in this group, time is required to discuss therapeutic issues with the physician.

TABLE 1 · COST-MINIMIZATION ANALYSIS OF DIFFERENT ANTIBIOTIC PROGRAMS*

	Average costs and average occurrences per patient per group		
	Extensive intervention	Pharmacist review of C & S	No intervention
Lab tests			
No. of labs	4.5	4	5
Average cost	$25	$25	$25
Total	**$113**	**$100**	**$125**
Drugs			
Oral	$70	$60	$50
Intravenous	$110	$104	$155
Total	**$180**	**$164**	**$205**
Physician costs			
Cost/visit	$30	$30	$30
No. of visits	6.5	4.2	6.1
Total	**$195**	**$126**	**$183**
Pharmacist time			
Hourly salary	$30	$30	$30
No. of minutes	45	55	0
Total	**$23**	**$28**	**$0**
Length of stay			
No. of days	4	3	3.8
Marginal cost	$550	$550	$550
Total	**$2,200**	**$1,650**	**$2,090**
Total average cost/patient	**$2,711**	**$2,068**	**$2,603**

* From an HMO perspective

Formulary/Source: L. Basskin, PharmD

Pharmacist review of culture and sensitivity reports. For this arm, drug therapy is reviewed 24 to 48 hours after empiric therapy has begun. No attempt will be made to change the empiric therapy. Instead, pharmacists will obtain all C & S reports of a select group of eligible patients receiving one of the drugs in question. If the drug being used either does not cover the cultured organisms or has a broader spectrum than necessary, a more appropriate or additional drug will be recommended to the prescribing physician.

No intervention. In this control arm of the study, a randomized selection of inpatients who meet the inclusion criteria for the study will be evaluated. Patients for whom a recommendation was made, either based on the C & S or empirically, and for whom the recommendation was not followed, also will be placed into this group.

DETERMINING RESULTS

The results of the study, using hypothetical numbers, are shown in table 1.

Therapy costs for each group were determined from a review of each patient's records, and the average for each group was calculated. Let's look at each category and examine how these costs were derived.

To determine laboratory costs, one could obtain the number of lab tests ordered directly from the computerized patient profile. Determining lab costs can be difficult, since many institutions don't calculate the cost of individual labs.

In my experience, there is a simple and fairly accurate way of estimating these costs. I start with the patient charge for each lab test and estimate the institution's cost by applying a typical "cost-to-charge" ratio. Since most laboratory costs do not differ substantially, I multiply the total number of lab tests by the average cost. Using an average lab test cost and the "cost-to-charge" ratio should result in a fair approximation of the total lab cost.

In the example of Pharmacist C & S review, an average of 4 labs were required per patient. If the average lab charge was $50, and the institution used a cost-to-charge ratio of 50%, then the average cost per lab test is $25. Therefore, average lab costs per patient would be $100.

To determine the cost of drugs, calculate the institution's drug acquisition cost, then add a reasonable amount to cover administration costs for each oral and intravenous dose. I used this approach since I wanted to know the total cost of therapy, and it's quite possible that the drugs ordered (at least initially) might be more expensive than the drugs subsequently prescribed.

In our HMO setting, the cost per physician visit was calculated as $30, based on an assumption that the doctor is paid a salary of $120,000 per year, works 2,000 hours per year, and requires 30 minutes per patient visit ($120,000/2,000 × 0.5 hours).

The cost of the pharmacist's intervention is based on the time involved with each patient. The average number of minutes required per patient is then multiplied by the hourly salary plus benefits. For example, under the extensive intervention alternative, the average intervention requires 45 minutes (0.75 hours). At $30 per hr, the average cost is $22.50 ($30/hr × 0.75 hours).

To determine length of stay costs, calculate the marginal costs (see Chapter One [1996;31:399-403]). In this analysis, I used a marginal cost of one day's stay at $550.

The next step is to compare the results and make a decision. Using the hypothetical numbers, you can see the average cost of therapy is lowest when the pharmacist reviews the C & S. Notice that the cost of extensive pharmacist interventions was actually higher than the cost of no interventions at all. This is because the extra labor cost and higher drug costs of the intervention were not offset by a decrease in length of stay or physician visits.

The last step is to calculate the number of full-time equivalents (FTEs) required to implement the recommendation I offer to our reader. Assuming a cost of $28 per pharmacist intervention per patient, and an expected number of patients for whom antibiotics will be ordered (based on the expected census) of 10,000 next year, new pharmacist FTE costs of $280,000 would be required. However, these expenses would be offset by lower lab test, drug, physician, and length of stay costs compared with the money spent if no interventions were taken (see table 2).

CONCLUSION

In this chapter, I've shown how it is possible to use pharmacoeconomic analysis to compare the costs and benefits of alternative interventions for a variety of diseases but for one class of drugs. A study was designed to try and reduce the time and costs of getting the patient on the correct and most cost-effective drug regimen at the earliest possible date. Another study, possibly addressed in a future column, might look at the evaluation of several different therapeutic regimens for one disease state.

How to calculate the costs of drug preparation, delivery and administration

Learning Objectives:

After reading this chapter, one should be able to:

1. Identify the cost components (or health care resources used) in preparing, distributing and administering each of oral, IV or IM push, and small volume parenteral dosage forms.

2. Measure the labor required, and the prevalence of use for each healthcare resource, for each of the aforementioned dosage forms.

3. Use the technique described in this chapter to determine the preparation, distribution and administration costs per dose and per day for different drug regimens/dosage forms.

You've mentioned previously that all drug costs should be included when comparing therapies. As a result of a reorganization, pharmacists in my institution now report to the head of radiology. My new boss thinks that the costs of preparing and delivering drugs to the patient are insignificant and should be excluded. Could you please comment further on this topic and give an example of how to incorporate these costs which I suspect are significant—into a pharmacoeconomic analysis?

GG
Director of Pharmacy
New Orleans

Whenever one compares the costs of alternative drug therapies, it's important to consider all associated costs. These obviously include the costs of the drug itself, but also include the costs of pharmacy administration, microbiology and radiology, storage and recordkeeping, and all diagnostic and monitoring tests that need to be performed. In this chapter, I'll present how to identify and calculate drug preparation, delivery, and administration costs; how to use these costs in a pharmacoeconomic analysis; and ultimately show that these costs are not insignificant.

THE TRUTH ABOUT FOUR COMMONLY HELD MYTHS

Unlike our reader's boss, it's my opinion that the cost of a drug—and the resultant outcome of a pharmacoeconomic analysis—can fluctuate widely depending on a drug's route of administration and preparatory and administration costs. Before discussing the specifics of how to collect and analyze these drug costs, however, I'd first like to dispel some commonly held beliefs.

Myth 1. Drug administration costs represent an insignificant portion of the total cost of therapy. While it's tempting to disregard these costs as too small ("how much can a label cost, anyway?"), "insignificant" is a relative term. For instance, the cost of commonly used antibiotics such as penicillin, erythromycin, and gentamicin is pennies per dose. In these cases, it is not unusual to find that the related administration costs exceed the cost of the drugs themselves. Using a cost-minimization approach, the drug to select in this type of scenario would be the one associated with the lowest preparation and administration costs.

However, even if the costs of administration are small relative to drug acquisition costs, these costs can become significant when multiplied by the total patient population who could be potential recipients of the drug. For example, in a 250-bed hospital with an average census of 80%, the annual number of inpatient days is approximately 73,000. If each person received one parenteral drug per day, with an average administrative cost of $4.00 per dose, administration costs would total $292,000 per year—hardly an insignificant figure.

Myth 2. Drug preparation, delivery, and administration costs do not differ significantly between drugs. It's hard to believe the cost of delivering a capsule in a unit dose form would be the same as that required to dissolve a powder and administer the drug by nasogastric tube; or, that the cost of giving an intramuscular rapid bolus is the same as that required to prepare a small volume parenteral or piggyback and infusing it over 30 minutes. While it may be true that the costs of dispensing similar drugs in your institution are nearly the same, that's a dangerous assumption to make without actually performing the analysis.

Myth 3. Labor and equipment costs are fixed, not variable, and should be excluded from pharmacoeconomic analyses. If the time frame under consideration is very short (e.g., less than 1 week), then virtually all labor and equipment costs are fixed since these costs cannot be either increased or decreased in response to changes in volume in this short time frame. In this case, the costs should probably be excluded from the cost of administering, preparing, or delivering drugs.

However, if the relevant time frame is longer (e.g., more than 1 month), then it is easier to change the labor and equipment costs in response to or anticipation of changes in patient or drug volume. The same costs that were treated as fixed in a short-term analysis can be treated as variable when the costs can be changed in response to volume. Nurses' schedules can be and are adjusted to take into account the census of the hospital. Pharmacists and technicians are added or removed from shifts depending on patient volume or number of pharmacy orders. Drug delivery pumps and similar devices are added or sold in response. Even entire wings or floors of a hospital can be closed if there is a decrease in patient census.

As a result of the flexibility institutions have in making rapid changes in labor and overhead, costs that may have been traditionally viewed as fixed should actually be considered variable, as long as some control exists for

TABLE 1	SPREADSHEET TO TRACK PREPARATION, DELIVERY AND ADMINISTRATION TIMES FOR DIFFERENT DRUG DELIVERY METHODS			
	Pharmacist	**Technician**	**Registered nurse**	**Nursing assistant**
Small volume parenteral				
Large volume porenteral				
IV Bolus				
IM Bolus				
IV continuous infusion w/pump				
IV slow push				

Formulary/Source: L. Basskin, PharmD

changing them in response to changes in activity in the relevant time period. Therefore, in my opinion, if an analysis of drug administration costs involves a projection for longer than a 1-month time frame, all material, labor, and equipment costs should be considered variable costs and should be factored into any pharmacoeconomic analysis.

Myth 4. It's too difficult or too time consuming to calculate drug administration costs for each pharmacoeconomic analysis undertaken. The time required to calculate the administration costs can be minimized if one has a plan and proceeds in an organized manner. Time can also be minimized if one calculates drug preparatory and administration times of only a few health care professionals; however, one risks loss of accuracy if the sample size is not representative of the full range of variation that may exist.

Also, it's not necessary to calculate these administration costs each time a pharmacoeconomic analysis is performed. Costs for all drug administration routes used in your institution can be calculated once, or as needed as significant changes in salaries, equipment or supply costs, or the productivity or utilization of existing staff or equipment occurs. These costs can then be used for any subsequent pharmacoeconomic analysis undertaken.

PERFORMING THE ANALYSIS

The steps to collecting and calculating the costs associated with drug preparation, delivery, and administration are straightforward.

First, identify the methods of drug delivery to be analyzed. For example, the costs of administering a drug by each of the following routes could be calculated: intravenous drip by pump, intramuscular or IV rapid push, IM or IV slow push, patch, paste, unit dose—oral, continuous infusion, rectal, nasal or still other routes also could be considered.

Next, for each drug delivery route, identify the cost of labor, supplies, and equipment.

TABLE 2 **TIME REQUIRED TO PREPARE AND DELIVER A BATCH OF 30 SVP***

Time/cost component for preparation of 30 SVP	Pharmacist	Technician
Receive, enter orders into computer, and verify	15 min	45 min
Resolve drug-related problems	7 min	0
Gather drugs and add diluents	0	20 min
Collect syringes, needles, and labels	0	12 min
Prepare SVP	10 min	30 min
Check accurocy	10 min	6 min
Deliver to floor	0	15 min
Check drug to order	0	12 min
Obtain pump	0	10 min
Total time	42 min = 0.7 hr	150 min =2.5 hr
Hourly rate	$30/hr	$ 15/hr
Total cost	$21	$37.50
Labor prep and delivery cost/drug	$0.70	$ 1.25

*SVP = small volume parenteral

Formulary/Source: L. Basskin, PharmD

Labor costs. To determine labor costs, keep track of the number and type of people who touch the drug from preparation to administration. The labor cost is simply the average salary and benefits of the person who handles the drug multiplied by the number of minutes the drug was handled.

To determine handling time, I suggest setting up a chart that depicts all possible methods of drug administration and personnel who might handle the drug at your institution. A section of such a chart is shown in table 1.

Several different methods can be used to track the amount of handling time required for each administration route. These include self-reporting by the individual, averaging the time for batch preparation, and using a third person to record times with a stop watch. The most accurate method to determine administration time is probably to track the *administration* time of several different people for each drug delivery route. Since many drugs are prepared and delivered in batches, it might be best to calculate the average time required to prepare and deliver a type of drug after identifying the time required for the entire batch.

Let's examine the completed chart shown in table 2. At this institution, most small volume parenteral (SVP) orders are made up in batches daily. The total and average time for the technicians to gather the drugs, needles, syringes, and other materials is determined and then converted into dollars. The total cost of pharmacist and technician labor for each drug unit in a 30-unit batch of SVP is $0.70 and $1.25, respectively, for a total cost per SVP of $1.95.

Supply costs. This includes the costs of nonreusable items needed to prepare and administer a drug, such as syringes and needles, diluents, IV ad-

	Drug A SVP	Drug A Premixed SVP	Drug B Slow push	Drug C Rapid push
Drug cost per vial	$5	$5	$5	$5
Number of mg/vial	250	100	100	50
Mg/dose	100	100	50	25
Doses per vial	2.5	1	2	2
Cost per dose	$2	$5	$2.50	$2.50
Doses/day	2	2	3	4
Drug cost/day	$4	$10	$7.50	$10

TABLE 3 ACQUISITION COST OF H2 BLOCKERS UNDER CONSIDERATION

Formulary/Source: L. Basskin, PharmD

ministration sets, gloves, sterile wipes, labels, and heparin/saline flushes. The costs assigned are the hospital's acquisition costs.

When determining the costs of delivering the drug, I find it helpful to follow the flow of physical goods from the warehouse to the patient. Once I've listed each supply item involved and the quantity used, it's easy to obtain the institution's acquisition costs.

Equipment costs. Unlike labor and supply costs, there are no readily identifiable costs per patient associated with medical equipment.

To calculate equipment costs, allocate the portion of the annual lease or total cost of the piece of medical equipment attributable to one patient's use. To derive this figure, one needs to project either the number of times per year (either the number of days or number of individual patient uses) the piece of medical equipment will be used. The annual lease cost is then divided by the expected number of uses per year to determine a cost per use. For example, if a drug delivery pump costs $2,450 per year to lease, and it will be used twice daily every day, the expected usage per year will be 730 (365 days X 2 uses per day), with a cost per usage of $3.35 ($2,450 ÷ 730).

When equipment is purchased (rather than leased), my recommended approach is to determine a yearly charge by dividing the cost of the equipment by the number of years it is expected to last before it is no longer functional or becomes obsolete. The per patient cost for use of the equipment is then determined using the same technique as described for leased equipment in the preceding paragraph. For example, a drug delivery pump costing $3,750 that is expected to last 3 years would have an annual cost of $1,250 per year divided among the expected uses or users for that year.

PULLING IT ALL TOGETHER

Let's try an example in which the costs of preparing, delivering, and administering drugs are considered when evaluating drugs for formulary inclusion. Suppose your institution wants to select one IV H2 blocker for the formulary—the least expensive one—and then will therapeutically substitute all other prescribed IV H2 blockers for the formulary agent selected.

Although you've conducted a literature review of the IV H2 blockers, you are hesitant to rely too heavily on the results of some of these published studies due to several problems that you've identified in study designs. First, the cost of these drugs are often incorrectly compared on a mg-per-mg or vial-to-vial basis. Not only are the H2 blockers of different potencies, but they are dosed at different frequencies so that the total number of mg per day can differ substantially. Different sized vials also make 3 comparisons among drugs very difficult. Another problem is that these drugs are prepared and administered in substantially different manners. For these reasons, any analysis of this drug class needs to include the costs of drug preparation and administration.

Let's look at three hypothetical H2 blockers under formulary consideration (FYI: the dose regimens and methods of administration are not FDA approved in this example). Consistent with the existing medical literature, we'll assume the drugs are equally effective for the prophylaxis of stress ulcers in the inpatient setting. The second assumption we'll make, though more controversial, is that the incidence of side effects, dosage adjustments in renal failure, and drug interactions are equal among all three agents.

Since all alternatives are equally effective, I'll use cost-minimization analysis to identify and select the alternative with the lowest possible costs. I'll consider the analysis from the perspective of the institution. Costs will include all drug, labor, supply, and equipment costs associated with the purchase, preparation, delivery, and administration of the drug to the patient. To simplify this example, I've selected $5.00 as the drug cost per vial and as the cost of a premixed IV bag.

Drug A, which is available in both proprietary and generic formulations, is given twice daily as a piggyback or SVP over 30 minutes. The drug can be bought in a premixed bag or it can be reformulated with diluent and injected into the piggyback. An infusion pump is required.

Drug B, available only as a proprietary name product, is administered three times daily as a slow intravenous push over 15 minutes. No diluent or SVP is required. A saline or heparin flush is recommended after administration.

Drug C can be administered several ways. It can infused by pump over 24 hours concurrently with another intravenous fluid, such as normal saline, D5W, or total parenteral nutrition. It can be given with an SVP, or it can be given as a rapid injection, followed by a saline or heparin flush. It is available in single-dose vials and must be administered four times daily. In this example, Drug C will be given as a rapid bolus infusion.

In table 3, I've calculated the daily acquisition cost of the drugs. I've broken that down into the number of mg per dose, cost per dose of drug, number of doses required per day, and the total cost of drug per day of therapy.

In table 4, I've calculated the preparation, distribution, and administration costs for each drug in in our example. For labor costs, I've estimated the number of minutes required for a pharmacist, technician, and nurse to prepare, deliver, and administer each drug. In this example, Drug A requires addition of a diluent to the vial and injection into an SVP (unless purchased in the premixed form), delivery of the SVP to the floor, hookup to the pump,

TABLE 4 DRUG ADMINISTRATIVE COSTS	Drug A SVP	Drug A Premixed SVP	Drug B Slow push	Drug C Rapid push
Labor (hourly salary)				
Pharmacist (prep)	$32.00	$32.00	$32.00	$32.00
Technician (delivery)	$16.00	$16.00	$16.00	$16.00
Nurse (administer)	$21.00	$21.00	$21.00	$21.00
Labor (minutes needed to prepare, deliver, administer drugs)				
Pharmacist (prep)	1.6	0.5	0	0
Technician (delivery)	1	1	1	0.5
Nurse (administer)	3.3	3.3	6	1.5
Labor (salary per minute X No. of minutes needed to prepare, deliver, administer drugs)				
Pharmacist (prep)	$0.85	$0.27	$0.00	$0.00
Technician (delivery)	0.27	0.27	0.27	0.13
Nurse (administer)	1.16	1.16	2.10	0.53
Total labor costs	**$2.28**	**$1.70**	**$2.37**	**$0.66**
Supplies: Preparation materials				
Diluent	$0.10	$0.00	$0.00	$0.00
Piggyback	0.50	0.00	0.00	0.00
Label	0.02	0.02	0.02	0.02
Syringe	0.22	0.22	0.00	0.00
Needle	0.11	0.11	0.00	0.00
Total prep supply costs	**$0.95**	**$0.35**	**$0.02**	**$0.02**
Supplies: Administration materials				
Saline Rush	$0.00	$0.00	$0.14	$0.14
Needle and syringe	0.00	0.00	0.11	0.11
Supply set/dose	2.25	2.25	0.00	0.00
Gloves and wipe	0.43	0.43	0.43	0.00
Needle	0.11	0.11	0.00	0.43
Total admin supply costs	**$2.68**	**$2.68**	**$0.68**	**$0.68**
Equipment				
Pump costs	**$3.35**	**$3.35**	**$0.00**	**$0.00**
Total prep, delivery, and, admin costs per day	**$9.26**	**$8.08**	**$3.07**	**$1.36**
Number of doses per day*	2	2	3	4
Total prep, delivery, and, admin costs per day	**$18.52**	**$16.16**	**$9.21**	**$5.44**
Total drug costs per day†	**$22.52**	**$26.16**	**$16.71**	**$15.44**

* from table 3
† includes drug acquisition cost from table 3

Formulary/Source: L. Basskin, PharmD

and transport of the pump.

Results. The results of the analysis reveal the following:

■ When examining drug acquisition costs alone (table 3), Drug A (given as a SVP) is the least expensive, with a daily acquisition cost of $4.00. Drug B has a higher acquisition cost than Drug C ($7.50 versus $10.00); and Drug C and Drug A (premixed SVP) are the most expensive at $10.00 each.

■ When examining drug preparation, delivery, and administration costs per dose (table 4), Drug C is the least expensive ($1.36), followed by Drug B ($3.07), Drug A premixed SVP ($8.08), and Drug A SVP ($9.26).

■ When examining drug preparation, delivery, and administration costs per day (table 4), the order remains the same: Drug C is least expensive ($5.44), followed by Drug B ($9.21), Drug A premixed SVP ($16.16), and Drug A SVP ($18.52).

■ When examining total drug cost per day (table 4), once again, Drug C is least expensive ($15.44) followed by Drug B ($16.71). Drug A SVP ($22.52) is third, and Drug A premixed SVP ($26.16) is the most expensive. In this example, I've shown that drug preparation, delivery, and administration costs are important and can change the outcome of a pharmacoeconomic evaluation. If acquisition cost alone was the determinant for formulary selection in our example, Drug A SVP would have been selected. However, by adding in drug preparation, delivery, and administration costs, in this example, Drug C—initially the most expensive drug based on acquisition cost—is determined to be the least expensive option and would be the drug I would recommend for formulary inclusion. In this example, Drug C's lower administration costs offset its higher acquisition cost.

How to evaluate the validity and usefulness of published randomized clinical trials

Learning Objectives:

After reading this chapter, one should be able to:

1. List the three elements of a study which should be evaluated before relying on study results when making a therapeutic decision.

2. List and describe nine essential tests of validity of a study.

3. List and explain the four points raised in this chapter which relate to the usefulness of a particular study.

In the last several columns, I've discussed how to perform outcomes research or pharmacoeconomic (PE) analyses to help decide between therapeutic alternatives or among competing clinical services. However, before (or instead of) designing and conducting your own PE study, you often need to first turn to the published literature—specifically, randomized clinical trials (RCTs)—to gain insights as to potential comparators, patient populations, outcomes to expect, and appropriate cost-effectiveness modeling techniques.

The three steps I recommend to critically review a RCT are to conduct the following:

■ *a macro assessment of the essential study components,*

■ *an assessment of the study's validity, and*

■ *an assessment of the study's usefulness.*

In this chapter, I'll provide details on each of these three steps.

DOES THE STUDY POSSESS ALL ESSENTIAL COMPONENTS?

In this first step, I suggest conducting a review of the core components of the RCT. These include the background or introduction, problem or goal, objectives, methodology, results, discussion, and conclusion. I've purposely omitted review of the abstract because I believe it often incorrectly summarizes the results or conclusions of the RCT. As far as I am concerned, the only purposes of an abstract are to allow one to gain some initial insights into an article and to identify articles for potential full review.

The components of a well-designed study logically and almost seamlessly flow together. For example, the *background* discusses different alternative therapies for treating a disease state and indicates where there may be room for improvement. The investigators then state what the specific therapeutic problem is that they will address in the context of the limitations of currently available options. The goal of the study should be to determine if the therapy being evaluated solved the problem better than either an alternative therapy or doing nothing at all.

EXHIBIT 1

Reasons to review randomized clinical trials (RCTs)

■ **To assess appropriate use of a drug for non-FDA-approved indications.** Quite often, a physician will want to know if a drug is effective in a non-FDA-approved indication—perhaps when conventional therapy has failed, for instance. The source of that information will usually be a published RCT, and one may have to rely on that as the sole basis for selection or rejection of the drug.

■ **To evaluate drugs for inclusion on the formulary or in disease pathways.** When being asked by the Formulary Committee to evaluate a drug or drug class for possible inclusion on the formulary or a disease state pathway, practitioners need an objective way of comparing the effectiveness of different drugs other than relying on anecdotal evidence or case reports. In such cases, the RCT will be one information source about the relative effectiveness of drugs.

■ **As a foundation for development of a sound pharmacoeconomic study.** When wanting to evaluate the cost-effectiveness of different medications or treatment regimens in a pharmacoeconomic analysis, more often than not, the pharmacoeconomic study you'd like to review has not yet been published or even conducted. In this case, you'll need to perform your own PE analysis using costs specific to your own institution. A good starting point in this process is to identify good, reliable, objective RCTs that evaluate the effectiveness of the drug and its comparators.

The *objectives* are a critical part of the study. They should be specific, measurable, and relevant subsets of the main goal and be worded such that if they are satisfied, then the goal has been met. The methodology should be designed around the objectives. Each objective must have a clearly defined method that will be followed to determine quantitatively if that objective can be satisfied.

The *results* section presents what happened after performing the methodology. The *discussion* section allows for an interpretation of the trends and interrelationships of the results of different tests and allow one to develop cause-and-effect relationships. The results and/or discussion section should also employ appropriate statistical analyses to let the reader know if any differences discovered were due to random sampling or are likely to be representative of differences that would be found when treating a much larger population.

The *conclusion* section should relate the discussion back to the original problem and tell readers if the therapy under study actually solved the problem. This section should also state any limitations of the study.

IS THE STUDY VALID?

The second step when evaluating a RCT is to assess the study's validity. The main issue to be addressed during this assessment is whether the study results (i.e., the effect) are really due to the drug under study (i.e., the cause) or due to some other cause or factor present among the study participants who received treatment.

It is important to note that there is no magic number of flaws above which a study is automatically deemed invalid. Instead, the reader has to look at the *number, severity,* and perhaps the *interrelatedness* of the flaws in the design to determine if any or all of them are so significant as to render the results invalid.

Personally, I assess a study's validity by considering each study result—each cause-and-effect relationship—against my own 9-point checklist. Interested readers might want to refer to other sources for further discussion of this approach.[1-3]

1. Study bias. Was the study designed to *intentionally* favor one drug or therapy over another? Obvious biases to look for include using subtherapeutic doses of a comparator drug and not blinding the investigators or patients as to which group (treatment or control) patients were randomized. More subtle ways of biasing a study include selecting tests and techniques designed to favor one group over another or choosing a measurement tool that shows an improvement in one group but is of no clinical significance. Watch for potential signs of bias and be extra careful of funded studies in which investigators could have a vested interest in the results.

2. Lack of placebo group/appropriate comparator. This is a major study flaw. If one wants to show that a treatment had a superior effect, one has to compare the results to a group that either received no treatment (i.e., placebo) or a different treatment. Without a placebo group, there is no guarantee that the results achieved in the study wouldn't have been achieved without any therapy (i.e., the patient might have reduced his blood pressure or gotten better by himself). If the study employs a comparator treatment, the comparator must be *appropriate*—i.e., one that the study drug would most likely replace on the formulary. While placebo-controlled studies may yield the most impressive results, I prefer RCTs that compare *appropriate* alternative drugs when more than one drug comparator is available.

3. Index of accomplishment. The criterion selected to determine if an objective is met is called the index of accomplishment (IOA). It should be a criterion that can be measured, validated (it measures what it purports to measure), and reproducible (the same measuring technique would yield the same results if used a second time). For example, if one wants to determine if a beta agonist inhaler improves an asthmatic patient's performance, the IOA needs to focus on specific aspects of performance, such as improvement in pulmonary function tests.

A common flaw is to select a surrogate marker as an IOA that may not be directly related to the objective. For example, suppose the objective of the RCT is to determine if treating patients with coronary artery disease with anti-angina drugs reduces mortality. Instead of measuring mortality, the investigators measured the extent of angina. The conclusion of the study should not discuss mortality. Because a surrogate IOA (angina) was used, there is no ev-

EXHIBIT 2

Shortfalls of some information sources

Some might ask why we simply can't rely on other sources and services that collect and summarize clinical trial information for us. The following are reasons why you should not rely too heavily on these respective information sources.

■ **Abstracts of published articles.** Short abstracts or summaries (such as those retrieved through the widely used Medline service) typically don't describe the type of patients enrolled in the trial—information you'll need to know if the study results are to be applied to your patient population. Relying on the abstract's reported conclusions requires you to assume the study was valid and reliable, a dangerous assumption to make if only reviewing the abstract rather than assessing the full text of the published trial. Finally, abstracts have often been found to incorrectly summarize the results and conclusions of their respective full-length trial reports.

■ **Secondary services (Micromedix).** These services only provide one- to three-sentence summations of the abstracts of published studies. These brief summaries are usually prepared by the service and often omit such critical information as potential design flaws and important information about methodology and characteristics of the patient population.

■ **Review articles summarizing randomized clinical trials.** Summaries of randomized clinical trials prepared by others are really only one author's interpretation of a study and its benefits. (Actually, even the original study investigators' interpretation of their own data could be quite different from the interpretation of others.) The major problem with review articles, however, is their potential to omit, gloss over, or give insufficient emphasis to design flaws or other noted limitations of RCTs.

idence—or the investigator must provide evidence— that decreased angina decreases mortality.

4. Measurement techniques. The IOA should be measured using the "gold standard" or the best available methodology. In addition, the method should yield the same result regardless of who measures it. Restated a different way, to minimize variability when different interpretations of the results are possible (e.g., reading an ECG), all persons responsible for reporting the results should receive the same training regarding use and interpretation of the measurement tool. Similarly, if the results are of a subjective nature (e.g., change in patients' quality of life or satisfaction), questioners should be trained in the same method, should ask the same questions, and should compare results of a sample measurement test to determine the degree of interquestioner variability. In summary, the validity of a RCT should be questioned if a study involves use of judgment and interpretation and the investigators do not explicitly state how potential inter-rater variability was reduced or eliminated.

5. Handling of patient noncompleters. A potential major study flaw is how "noncompleters" are handled. Common reasons why patients fail to complete a study are that they voluntarily drop-out, are too sick to continue, die, are lost to follow-up, meet an exclusion criterion of the study and are no longer eligible, or are unable to maintain compliance with the required drug and nondrug regimens and tests. Noncompleters are often those patients who are likely to be associated with the worst outcomes. Thus, it's important to assess the reasons cited for their exclusion from the final total group analysis. At times, it is appropriate to include patients even if they didn't complete the study. For example, in evaluating whether a drug was associated with intolerable side effects, those who dropped out may have done so because of those side effects.

Perhaps the best way to treat dropouts is to apply *intention-to-treat analysis*. Under this method, patients who drop out are categorized by: (a) their last score or measurement at the time they dropped out, (b) the average for the entire group, or (c) the worst score or measurement for the group. The study should indicate which of these methods was used and exactly how many people dropped out as well as why and when they dropped out. Again, if a RCT fails to appropriately evaluate those who only partially completed the study, some significant results may be omitted and study conclusions may be invalid.

6. Duration of the study. Another flaw of many studies is that they measure results too infrequently or after too short a time period. A study's duration should reflect its objectives. For example, if the goal is to determine if a drug *prevents* disease reoccurrences, then adequate time must be allowed for the disease to reoccur before ending the study. If a study's goal is to measure impact on mortality, then a long time frame is needed. Keep in mind that even "long-term" is a subjective term. The Diabetes Control and Complications Trial, which followed insulin-dependent diabetic patients over 10 years,[4] is still criticized by some as failing to allow enough time to see all of the long-term complications of diabetes.

Another important point about study duration is that many undesirable effects of drug therapy take time to occur. These include addiction to a drug, development of tolerance to its effects (in which higher doses are needed or the drug becomes ineffective over time), noncompliance with therapy, or the appearance of adverse effects. For example, studies involving amiodarone are often designed to assess its onset of effect. However, these studies are often not of long enough duration to catch the pulmonary toxicities associated with its use—toxicities that one would want to consider when undertaking a complete assessment of the drug. In summary, the message is to review the time frame of the study and determine if sufficient time has been allowed for the appearance of both desirable and undesirable events.

7. Confounding variables. To establish true cause-and-effect relationships in a study, it's necessary to exclude or account for other reasons why a drug or therapy may have been associated with a certain effect. These confounding variables include such factors as age, sex, weight, concurrent drug therapy, concomitant disease states, diet, amount of sleep, and economic issues.

EXHIBIT 3

Checklist of questions to ask when evaluating RCTs

Level 1: Macro assessment of the study's core components
■ Are all the core components—background/introduction, problem/ goal, objectives, methodology, results, discussion, conclusion—present?

Level 2: Assessment of the study's validity
■ Is there evidence of study bias?

■ Does the study include a placebo group (to determine if treatment is equal or superior to no treatment) or an *appropriate* comparator?

■ Are the criteria used to determine if objectives have been met clearly identified?

■ Are measurement tools that are used the "gold standard" or well-accepted methodology? Has variability in measurements been minimized and/or controlled for?

■ How were patients who did not complete the study reported in the analysis of the total study?

■ Is the study of sufficient duration to allow for objectives to be met and for both desirable and undesirable events to occur?

■ How are potential confounding variables—differences in patient age, weight, concurrent drug therapies, concomitant disease states—handled in the study?

■ Is the study statistically valid?

■ How was patient compliance ensured?

Level 3: Assessment of the study's usefulness for your own practice setting
■ Are the results reliable and reproducible?

■ Do the study problems and goals mirror yours?

■ Are side effects tolerable?

■ Does your patient population resemble that of the study?

There are two easy methods to account for and to try to eliminate the effects of confounding variables.

The first method is to exclude patients with many of these factors. The drawback of this approach is that it often becomes difficult to extrapolate the study results to a real-world patient population with all its diversities.

A different approach is to not limit the enrollment of the study but to instead randomize patients with all of their many confounding variables between the groups. If the sample size is large enough, randomization produces equal-sized groups that are internally diverse but similar to each other in makeup (i.e., have the same number of patients receiving other drug therapies, same numbers of each sex, etc.). Of course, the RCT should discuss the characteristics of each group and state if a significant difference existed between the groups after randomization with respect to any of these confounding variables.

EXHIBIT 4

Practicum: Can you spot this RCT's strengths and flaws ?

After reading this chapter, have you improved your article evaluation skills? Let's find out! The following passage describes a fictitious RCT. Your task is to evaluate its validity and usefulness. I'll publish my own evaluation as Appendix I to this book.

You are responsible for selecting one of the many benzodiazepines (BDZs) for sleep assistance for formulary inclusion. Your objective is to select a drug that has a quick onset, a duration sufficient to last through the night, a mild side effect profile, and a low cost. An initial search of the published literature reveals that no BDZ can claim superior effectiveness. However, a new article has just been published that touts the effectiveness of a new drug, Snorazapam. A quick review of the article abstract reveals that in this study, Snorazapam was "more effective" than its comparators and costs less. Before running to the P & T Committee, you read the details of the study, which are described as follows:

The objective of the study was to determine if Snorazapam was more effective than its competitors. Two other drugs were chosen as comparators. To avoid adverse effects, all three drugs were dosed initially at one-half their usual strength, but patients who requested another dose were able to receive one. Patients who were asleep at the time the pill was to be administered were not awakened to take the pill. No attempt was made to disguise the identity of the drug product. All patients receiving any of the three medications received instructions on relaxation and other techniques to fall asleep.

Patients were selected from among the practices of a variety of physicians who admit patients. Physicians were allowed to designate the group to which their patient could be assigned until the maximum enrollment limit of 50 patients per group was reached. When the demographics of the patients were examined at study conclusion, it was found that a significant number of patients in one of the comparator drug groups were also receiving drugs that may be associated with a transient CNS stimulating effect.

After 1 week, all study participants were interviewed by an unbiased, trained investigator who knew which study drug had been received by each patient. He asked each patient the same questions about the quality of their sleep and the occurrence of any side effects. If the patient didn't understand the question, the investigator could explain it further.

The results showed that Snorazapam was associated with a faster onset and longer duration of sleep. There were some reports of nausea and hallucinations with all three drugs, but these were noted as "unsolicited and anecdotal" and were neither quantified nor broken down by drug.

8. Statistical validity. It's important that appropriate statistical analysis be used to ensure that differences between treatment groups were not due to chance or to a random sampling error (e.g., was the real patient population appropriately represented in the sample selected?). It's equally important to know that the sample size was large enough to detect a difference when results indicate that no differences were discovered between treatment groups.

Traditionally, for a difference to be deemed "statistically significant," the chance that the difference is due to sampling has to be less than 1 in 20, or $p < 0.05$. Thus, the "p value" should be provided for all differences cited.

Another common statistical error occurs when the wrong statistical test is used for the type of data gathered. Interested readers may wish to consult an introductory biostatistics textbook for more specific discussion on the test types.[5]

9. Compliance. When one therapy outperforms another, a common assumption is that the dosage regimen used was realistic. As any health care professional knows, when drugs produce toxic or noxious side effects, require too frequent dosing, or are uncomfortable to take, patients are less likely to comply with the therapy as prescribed. Thus, a study should be designed to ensure compliance via such tools as individual follow-up or pill counts, and it should report any incidences of discovered noncompliance.

IS THE STUDY USEFUL?

The final step in evaluating a RCT is to assess its usefulness in terms of potential application to your own patient population. I ask myself the following four questions in this phase of RCT assessment:

1. Are the results reliable and reproducible? Using the methods employed by the study investigators, the results of a study should be able to be reproduced in a real world patient population. Sometimes difficulties can arise, however, if the study's follow-up and patient interaction are so extensive that it is financially impossible to repeat the study. In this case, one needs to feel confident that if the study could be repeated, the results would be the same.

2. Do the study problems and goals mirror yours? Carefully read the goals and objectives of the study and make sure they are ones that you have for your patients. Otherwise, you may recommend therapy designed to solve a problem that isn't as high of a priority for your patients. For example, if your goal is to *prevent* reoccurrence of a urinary tract infection (UTI), don't rely on a study that found a drug to be effective in *treating* a UTI—your objective will not be accomplished.

3. Are side effects tolerable? Most studies are not designed to assess the frequency of adverse effects or the impact of those effects on patient compliance. Instead, after reporting the benefits of the drug in each group, toxicities—including mortality and morbidity—are usually reported in a separate table as "additional information." It is your job to assess if the impact of those side effects outweighs the benefits of drug therapy because of patient noncompliance or even the possibility of patient death.

For example, two well-known drugs, Augmentin (amoxicillin and clavulanic acid) and Cytotec (misoprostol), have been shown to be effective in treating certain types of infectious disease and preventing NSAID-induced GI bleeding, respectively. However, experienced practitioners know that both drugs are associated with major and persistent diarrhea in up to 40% of patients, which often leads patients to stop therapy on their own, or requires them to return to their physician for a change in therapy.

4. Does your patient population resemble that of the study? Finally, it's important to remember that most RCTs exclude many of the confounding variables described earlier in this paper in order to show a cause-and-effect relationship between the drug being studied and the desired outcome. However, more often than not, your patients have concomitant disease states or are taking concurrent drug therapies. Either of these factors could be reasons why the drug, if used in your setting, may not be a suitable choice or may be ineffective. Thus, it's very important to read the study's inclusion criteria, which describe the characteristics of the patients enrolled, and compare them with the particular patient population you had intended to target.

CONCLUSION

The purpose of this chapter was to discuss how to interpret the primary literature—the randomized clinical trial. I've discussed the essential elements of a study that should be present and the typical flaws that make a study and its results either invalid or of little practical use. Understanding the basic components of a well-designed and -implemented study is essential if one is to move on to the next step—evaluating the merits of a pharmacoeconomic study.

In the next chapter, I'll discuss exactly that; i.e., how to assess a pharmacoeconomic study or analysis and what additional components need to be included in this type of study. I'll also discuss ways to work with the information in these studies to make it more applicable to your setting when your patient population and costs of therapy are not identical to those of the study investigators.

REFERENCES

1. Elenbaas RM, Elenbaas JK, Cuddy PG. "Evaluating the medical literature" (part 1): Abstract, introduction, methods. Ann Emerg Med 1983;12:549-55.
2. Elenbaas RM, Elenbaas JK, Cuddy PG. "Evaluating the medical literature" (part 3): Results, discussion. Ann Emerg Med 1983;12:679-83.
3. Friedman LM, Furberg CD, DeMetz DL, eds. "Fundamentals of Clinical Trials" (3rd edition). St. Louis: Mosby, 1996.
4. The Diabetes Control and Complications Trial Research Group. "The effect of intensive treatment of diabetes on the development and progress of long-term complications in insulin-dependent diabetes mellitus." N Engl J Med 1993;329:977-86.
5. Dawson-Saunders B, Trapp R, eds. Basic & Clinical Biostatistics (2nd edition). Norwalk, CT: Appleton & Lange, 1994.

How to evaluate the validity and usefulness of pharmacoeconomic literature

Learning Objectives:

After reading this chapter, one should be able to:

1. List and explain the essential elements of a pharmacoeconomic study.

2. Explain why standards or guidelines are recommended for pharmacoeconomic studies or published literature.

3. Explain the importance of disclosure, over selection, of methodology in a pharmacoeconomic analysis.

As we move more toward an evidence-based approach in medicine, we'll need proof for everything we do. In the context of this journal, knowledge of PE issues provides Formulary Committees with evidence-based information upon which to select drugs for the formulary or for disease state pathways. Other ways in which knowledge of PE can be put to use include:

■ to analyze and compare the results of one published PE study with another,

■ to adapt a currently existing study (e.g., replacing study costs and assumptions with your own practice setting's information) to determine how results and recommendations may change in your organization,

■ to conduct your own outcomes research or PE study, mirroring the approach used in a published study to solve a similar problem at your practice setting,

■ to solve problems associated with difficult-to-measure areas, such as quality of life or intangible costs, or

■ to apply any of a variety of PE techniques and models to solve problems in unrelated clinical areas.

In summary, a sound understanding of key PE concepts and principles permits assessment of the validity and usefulness of PE literature when time, financial, or staff limitations make it infeasible to conduct such studies yourself. Thus, if the reality is that we must rely on the work of others, we must be able to accurately assess these works.

HOW TO ASSESS THE PHARMACOECONOMIC LITERATURE

What are the essential elements of a PE study? Before presenting my personal checklist, it's important to remind readers that there are no universally accepted guidelines or principles for conducting—and therefore for our purposes, reviewing—PE studies. In fact, within the medical and pharmacoeconomic community, there is a great divergence of opinion with respect to the

EXHIBIT 1

Principal ways in which a PE study differs from a randomized clinical trial

In Chapter 12, I discussed how to assess the validity and usefulness of published randomized clinical trials (RCTs). The techniques used for reviewing a PE study are similar to those for reviewing an RCT. However, due to the lack of standards and guidelines and the nature of PE evaluations, an extra level of caution or interpretation on the part of the reader is required beyond that required for an RCT. Elements that are unique to a PE study and/or require critical assessment include the following:

■ **Definitions** of potentially ambiguous terms such as "cost," "effectiveness" or "efficacy," and "cost-effective" therapy,

■ **Assumptions** used when more than one acceptable analytical method is applied (e.g., choice of rate used for discounting, or extent of sensitivity analysis employed), and

■ **Rigor of the statistical analysis** employed by the PE study authors (such rigor is the standard by which results of RCTs are judged, but it is not often the level to which PE results are judged).

need for PE study standards. While guidelines or principles have been adopted by the governments of Canada, France (in progress), Australia, and New Zealand, progress in this area in the United States has been limited to guidelines developed by the Pharmaceutical Research and Manufacturers of America.[1] However, at the health plan level, at least one managed care organization has developed its own guidelines, which will be used to assist in its formulary decision-making process.[2]

Based on the work of several leading authors in this field,[3-8] I've developed the following list of key elements I look for when assessing the validity and usefulness of a published PE study. It is not necessary that the essential elements listed below be presented in either a specific order or be identified with distinct subheadings within the PE study (e.g., you might not find a subheading entitled "discounting" in a PE study). What *is* necessary, however, is that all the elements are considered and that all methods and assumptions are clearly stated.

■ **Definition of the problem.** Like a randomized clinical trial (RCT), a PE study should define the problem and briefly discuss the disease state and potential treatments. The reason for conducting the PE study and the hypothesis being tested or evaluated also should be clearly identified. Finally, the goals of the study, the specific objectives to be met, and the methodology used to achieve them should be presented.

As in an RCT, study elements such as double blinding, use of a control group, and randomization of patients should be employed. Additionally, information on the patient population enrolled—including a description of the inclusion and exclusion criteria—should be presented.

EXHIBIT 2

Do we need standards and guidelines to evaluate the PE literature?

The answer, in my opinion, is a resounding *yes*. Standards are needed because we can't rely on individuals to develop their own techniques of analysis and methods of reporting, for the following reasons:

1. Without standards, there are no rules to guide the method of analysis. This allows individuals to adopt whatever techniques they want to achieve the *desired* results.

2. There is no independent regulatory or accrediting organization—such as HCFA, JCAHO, NCQA, the FDA—reviewing and utilizing this information that could impart a "seal of approval" on the analysis. Without an objective and qualified third party reviewing a study's results and design, credibility may be lacking and the opportunity for biased reporting and biases in study design increases.

3. Without standards, it is difficult to compare PE analyses prepared by different authors or investigators.

4. Because PE is a relatively new science, many health care professionals are unfamiliar with the techniques and assumptions that need to be made and stated. Standardizing techniques and/or disclosure requirements would help those who are less educated in PE be more confident when relying on the results of such literature.

5. Many health care professionals adapt PE analyses by inserting their own costs into the published PE study. However, without standards, this practice becomes dangerous because one must assume (i.e., hope) that the study design and assumptions used are appropriate for every user.

6. Some people are wary of guidelines, which they believe will result in only one acceptable methodology and eliminate equally acceptable alternatives from consideration. I agree that there shouldn't be just one set of rules applied without thought to all PE evaluations. However, there needs to be a decrease in the number of "equally acceptable alternative methodologies" and an improvement or standardization of disclosure requirements (i.e., state your assumptions).

The concept of uniform guidelines for PE research and for evaluating PE literature has been addressed in the medical literature. Those who are interested in reading more should refer to these articles.[1,2,11,12] Also, the International Society for Pharmacoeconomics and Outcomes Research (ISPOR) is in the process of developing guidelines referred to as "GAPP" (generally accepted pharmacoeconomic principles). This matter will be discussed more fully at their annual meeting in Philadelphia later this month.

Also, since many of the assumptions of the effectiveness and/or the probabilities related to the outcomes used in PE studies are based on one or more RCTs, it is wise to be a little wary. The chance for bias and accidental error increases if certain results in one published RCT were excluded because data were missing or unavailable or if an unfavorable RCT was omitted.

■ **Identification of alternatives.** Comparator therapies should be relevant—i.e., they should be reasonable options to a problem, such as a drug that has been approved for treating the specific condition or a drug that is available for prescribing for which there is some evidence to support its use for this unapproved indication.

■ **Selection of appropriate outcomes or measures of effectiveness.** Outcomes need to be specific and measurable, must relate to the objectives of the study, and should be identified as either primary or secondary. For example, in considering alternative therapies for patients with congestive heart failure, the primary objective might be to determine which alternative is most cost effective in terms of reducing mortality. Secondary objectives might include determining which alternative is most cost effective in terms of improving quality of life, increasing exercise tolerance, or reducing acute exacerbations. All outcomes, both desired (positive outcomes) and adverse (negative outcomes, such as side effects), should be determined for each treatment alternative.

■ **Definition of types of costs.** The specific *types of costs* assessed must be clearly defined. For example, are intangible costs (e.g., pain and suffering) included? Do costs include direct patient care and indirect treatment costs (such as travel time or lost wages from work)? Are both fixed and variable costs included in the analysis? Is cost defined as actual dollars paid out or is it based on "notional value," such as the amount someone "might pay" to avoid an illness?

■ **Description of health care resources used (relevant cost components).** The specific components of each *type of cost* should be further specified. For example, "direct medical costs" could include all or some nursing care, lab tests, and physician visits. The units by which costs are measured should also be described. For example, duration of therapy could be in minutes in the postop unit or in days in the general medicine unit. Drug costs could be described as cost per dose, cost per day, or cost per typical course of treatment. Labor could be calculated in minutes or in days. This information is needed both to evaluate the appropriateness of the units used in the study and to determine the applicability of these measurements to those typically used at your practice setting.

Finally, costs should be measured or assigned value (i.e., cost components need to be assigned dollar amounts) in an appropriate manner, and the methods need to be disclosed. For example, were actual institutional costs used or those of a third party (i.e., actual drug acquisition and administration costs or AWP)? Were costs that are difficult to calculate (i.e., costs of daily inpatient care) actually calculated or computed using a cost-to-charge ratio?

The important point is that the PE study authors should clearly state all cost components and all units of measurement upon which costs were calculated. Be certain that any assumptions used to calculate costs are clearly stated and that you take the time to read them and critically evaluate them.

■ **Identification of study perspective.** As I've mentioned in previous

EXHIBIT 3

Checklist of essential elements that must be addressed in a PE study

- Definition of the problem
- Identification of alternatives
- Selection of appropriate outcomes or measures of effectiveness
- Definition of types of costs
- Description of relevant cost components
- Identification of study perspective
- Use of relevant study time frame
- Incorporation of sensitivity analysis
- Application of discounting, when appropriate
- Selection of an appropriate PE cost model or technique
- Calculation of cost-effective alternative, stated as absolute and as marginal or incremental difference

columns, the choice of perspective of the analysis is very important. The perspective chosen could be that of the patient, the institution, a third-party payer, or society at large. Well-crafted PE studies not only include a discussion of the perspective but will discuss the problem and solutions from more than one perspective. More important, however, is to assess that mixed perspectives are not used. For instance, a poorly crafted PE study may mix acquisition *costs* for drugs (the hospital's perspective of cost) with *charges* for drugs, length of stay, or surgery (the patient's perspective of cost).

■ **Use of relevant study time frame.** Each PE problem, like each therapeutic problem, has a relevant time frame based on its goals and objectives. For example, if the goal of a study is to determine the cost effectiveness of two drugs used to cure an infection, such as otitis media, a relevant time frame to evaluate costs and outcomes would be after 10 to 14 days, not after 1 day.

Consider two factors when assessing a PE study's time frame. First, only costs that will be incurred in the time frame (i.e., until the desired outcome of therapy is achieved) should be gathered.

Second, determine how fixed costs are handled. Studies often omit fixed costs in an analysis since, by definition, these costs are fixed and won't change regardless of the therapeutic alternative selected. However, fixed costs can sometimes be considered variable costs if the study's time frame is increased. For instance, a nurse's salary may be fixed for a week and, therefore, additional patients do not add to the hospital's cost of care. However, in a time frame exceeding 1 year, substantial changes could be made to both the number of nurses required on a medical unit and their salary requirements.

■ **Incorporation of sensitivity analysis.** Sensitivity analysis addresses uncertainty in data. The researchers change the primary variables through a range of plausible values to assess the effect on the overall decision. Results of a well-designed PE study should include sensitivity analysis to determine if results would change should an extreme value occur. For example, suppose a PE study was designed to determine the cost effectiveness of two antihypertensive drugs. Use of either drug would result in an average blood pressure reduction of 10 mm Hg; however, one drug's effectiveness ranged from -5 to -15 mm Hg, while the other drug's ranged from -25 to +5 mm Hg. If only the average blood pressure lowering effect were used (i.e., 10 mm Hg) and no sensitivity analysis was conducted, the study would be excluding the possibility that a +5 mm Hg increase in blood pressure could occur (and, possibly, also not be including the costs related to the occurrence of the "extreme" value).

■ **Application of discounting, when appropriate.** As discussed in Chapter 9, the need for a PE study to include discounting should be considered. The time value of money needs to be discounted when the amount of time between payments and/or benefits increases. For instance, when at least 3 to 5 years occur between payments, future cash flows should be converted into present-value dollars for the analysis to be more meaningful.

■ **Selection of an appropriate PE cost model or technique.** In previous chapters, I have referred to cost-minimization analysis (CMA), cost-effectiveness analysis (CEA), cost-benefit analysis (CBA), cost-utility analysis (CUA), and value analysis. The appropriate method must be selected based on the type of comparison to be made. For example, a CMA is appropriate only when each alternative has equal effectiveness. A CBA is appropriate only if all costs and benefits can be converted into dollar equivalents. A CEA is appropriate only when one nondollar measure of effectiveness is being considered. A CUA is appropriate for measuring a combination of subjective and objective variables, such as quality-of-life years. Value analysis[10] attempts to objectively and simultaneously measure several subjective variables, each with a different relative importance.

■ **Calculation of cost-effective alternative, stated as absolute and as marginal or incremental difference.** Using the proper model, it is obvious that the PE study authors will state which of the recommended alternatives is most cost effective. However, keep in mind that the most cost-effective agent may not be the agent that would—or should—necessarily be recommended for the formulary or used in clinical practice. For example, lovastatin costs $60 per month and reduces LDL cholesterol by 40 mg/dl ($1.50/month/unit), and fluvastatin costs $30 per month and reduces LDL cholesterol by 30 mg/dl ($1/month/unit). Fluvastatin, with a lower dollar per month per unit cost, is more cost effective than lovastatin. The extra cost per unit per month for lovastatin is $3 per unit per month ($60 minus $30/[40 minus 30 mg/dl]). Which drug is recommended depends on whether the extra $3 per unit per month is a price the payer is willing to pay to reduce the risk of coronary artery disease. It will also depend on the perceived clinical significance of obtaining a 30- versus 40-point reduction in LDL cholesterol.

REFERENCES

1. Clemens K, Townsend R, Luscombe F, et al. "Methodological and conduct principles of pharmacoeconomic research." <u>PharmacoEconomics</u> 1995;8:169-74.

2. Langley P, Sullivan S. "Pharmacoeconomic evaluations: Guidelines for drug purchasers." J Managed Care Pharm 1996;2:671-7.
3. Drummond M, Stoddart GL, Torrance GW. Methods for economic evaluation of health care programmes. Oxford: Oxford University Press, 1987.
4. Sacristan JA, Soto J, Galende I. "Evaluations of pharmacoeconomic studies." Ann Pharmacother 1993;27:1126-33.
5. Lee KT, Sanchez LA. "Interpretation of "cost-effective" and soundness of economic evaluations in the pharmacy literature." Am J Hosp Pharm 1991;48: 2622-7.
6. Udvarhelyi S, Colditz GA, Dai A, et al. "Cost-effectiveness and cost-benefit analyses in the medical literature." Ann Intern Med 1992;116:238-44.
7. Weinstein MC, Stason WB. "Foundations of cost-effectiveness analysis for health and medical practices." N Engl J Med 1997;336:716-21.
8. Jolicoeur LM, Jones-Grizzle AJ, Boyer JG. "Guidelines for performing a pharmacoeconomic analysis." Am J Hosp Pharm 1992;49:1741-7.
9. Basskin L. "Discounting in pharmacoeconomic analyses: When and how to do it." Formulary 1996;31:1217-27.
10. Basskin L. "Using value analysis to select formulary drugs from among similar agents." Formulary 1996;31:1083-90.
11. Torrance GW, Blaker D, Detsky A, et al. "Canadian guidelines for economic evaluation of pharmaceuticals." PharmacoEconomics 1996;9:535-59.
12. Langley P. "The November 1995 revised Australian guidelines for the pharmacoeconomic evaluation of pharmaceuticals." PharmacoEconomics 1996;9:341-52.

Using cost-benefit analysis to evaluate the cost-effectiveness of a specialty clinic

Learning Objectives:

After reading this chapter, one should be able to:

1. List typical problems associated with the measurement of each of cost and efficacy of a specialty clinic.

2. Design a study to assess the cost-effectiveness of a clinic, by selecting alternatives and identifying appropriate outcomes and healthcare resources for future measurement

3. Determine, using each of cost-benefit analysis and cost-effectiveness analysis, the desirability or value or operating a specialty clinic.

Dr. Basskin:

In an effort to decrease its costs, our HMO has decided to increase the number of clinics it operates. Our management believes that the cost of patient care can be reduced without a loss of efficacy by having patients receive preventative or maintenance care at specialty clinics—instead of waiting for acute problems to occur that require hospital admission.

The administration has asked the pharmacy and nursing departments to establish and operate an anticoagulation clinic on a trial basis for patients on warfarin therapy. We plan to monitor patients' lab values and other drug therapy, recommend regimen changes to physicians, and take steps to ensure that patients comply with their drug therapies. Our goal is to prevent both bleeding or thrombotic events due to over or under anticoagulation, respectively. However, to continue this clinic after the pilot phase, we'll need to prove that the benefits from operating the clinic are greater than the costs of developing, implementing, and operating it. How can we indeed determine if benefits exceed costs?

Signed

Dr. A.L.B.
Clinical Coordinator
Chicago, IL

Our reader's problem is one that is becoming more prevalent, for two reasons. It's true that many institutions have opened specialty clinics in an effort to detect or prevent patient health problems to ultimately avoid the costs of hospitalization. However, few controlled studies have yet adequately assessed whether the benefits of these clinics exceed their costs, nor have studies identified the most cost-effective services to offer (see Ex-

EXHIBIT 1

Types of problems seen in published studies involving specialty clinics

Common problems in study design to look for in published studies evaluating the cost effectiveness of specialty clinics include the following:

■ Failure to narrowly define and measure the outcomes. Often too many goals (e.g., educate patients, avoid adverse drug events, improve the drug regimen, reduce cost compared with individual physician management, improve dietary counseling, and increase patient convenience and satisfaction) are pursued simultaneously. Use of several interventions or clinic activities and obtainment of multiple outcomes make it difficult to determine which outcome resulted from which intervention. Additionally, if the published article is reporting on a pilot study, the clinic may have performed activities above and beyond what it will be doing in "real-world," day-to-day operations.

■ Failure to consider all of the costs of the clinic in the analysis (such as the cost of "free" drugs being given to patients to entice them to keep scheduled appointments).

■ Lack of a control group for comparison of the results.

■ Failure to first assess patient noncompliance with the drug regimen and to prospectively intervene to ensure compliance.

■ Failure to continue to assess patient compliance under realistic conditions—e.g., employing intensive patient compliance monitoring techniques in the early stages of a program (as in the pilot stage) that are not continued long term.

■ Failure to control for bias by using unblinded patients and investigators.

■ Failure to eliminate confounding variables such as concurrent drugs or disease states which could influence the results obtained.

■ Failure to calculate costs from a single perspective (e.g., mixing institutional costs with patient-incurred costs).

■ Failure to standardize the procedures used by investigators at the clinic or to assess the extent to which variability between the investigator methods may have affected the results.

hibit 1). The lack of published evidence about the cost effectiveness of specialty clinics means that each proposed clinic needs to be evaluated by its provider (both before and after implementation).

The second reason for the growth of specialty clinics is the desire to increasingly have nurses and pharmacists offer services traditionally provided by physicians. The argument is that this allows these services to be offered at a lower cost without loss of effectiveness.

Although it can be argued that feasibility studies can't be conducted for all programs on our "wish lists," it's for this very reason (i.e., finite funds) that the cost effectiveness of different funding options is compared. Those options with

EXHIBIT 2

Selected therapeutic and nontherapeutic outcomes to consider when establishing a specialty clinic

While the list of potential outcomes to consider when developing a specialty clinic seems endless, the most common categories of outcomes are:

Therapeutic:
- improvement of the drug regimen by making appropriate adjustments in dose, reducing or treating drug side effects and avoiding potential drug-drug and drug-food interactions by undertaking a complete drug therapy review
- improvement or cure of the disease (i.e., lower mortality)
- improvement of quality of life (i.e., lower mortality)
- avoidance of hospitalization by preventing reoccurrence or acute exacerbations of disease.

Sometimes "surrogate" outcomes are chosen (e.g., lab values or functioning tests) because they are easier to collect and quantify than clinical outcomes such as decreased morbidity (e.g., quality of life, physical functioning). However, if one chooses to rely on surrogate outcomes, there should be a clear correlation between the surrogate and clinical outcome. For example, studies have used cholesterol levels to assess the impact of cholesterol-lowering drugs on heart attacks because a clear relationship has been shown to exist between cholesterol levels and coronary artery disease.

Nontherapeutic:
- reduction in overall health care costs compared with individual physician management
- improvement of patient compliance with scheduled lab visits
- improvement of pharmacist-nurse-physician collaboration and professional relations by demonstrating each group's therapeutic skills to other members of the heath care team
- improvement of patient convenience and satisfaction
- improvement of the image and goodwill of the institution
- improvement of cash flow to the institution by billing the cost of monitoring and review of drug therapy to patients and third-party payers
- increase in the number of patients seen by the clinic
- creating a new source of jobs for pharmacists and nurses.

the greatest benefits for the dollars spent will be the ones that are eventually funded and maintained.

In beginning to explore an answer to this reader's question, the following questions need to be raised. The answers to these questions should be used in designing the clinic—i.e., determining which service to offer, the dollars to dedicate to clinic renovations and staffing, and the method by which the cost effectiveness will be evaluated.

TABLE 1	**USING COST-BENEFIT ANALYSIS TO EVALUATE THE ECONOMIC FEASIBILITY OF A SPECIALTY CLINIC***		
	Control group	Clinic group	Difference
No. of patients	300	300	0
Costs			
Operational			
Rent	$0	$24,000	$24,000
Renovations	0	8,000	8,000
Utilities	0	3,500	3,500
Supplies	0	6,500	6,500
Subtotal	$0	$42,000	$42,000
Salaries			
Administrator (½ time)	0	15,000	15,000
Pharmacist	0	48,000	48,000
Nurse	0	28,000	28,000
Physician†	72,000	9,000	(63,000)
Subtotal	$72,000	$100,000	$28,000
Monitoring costs			
Cost per PT test	$35	$10	
No. PT tests/year	4	4	
Subtotal (monitoring costs)	$42,000	$12,000	($30,000)
TOTAL WARFARIN MONITORING COSTS	$114,000	$154,000	$40,000
Benefits (health care costs saved)			
Hospital admits for bleeding	13,800	3,500	10,300
Treating thrombotic stroke	35,000	12,000	23,000
DVT and pulmonary embolism	61,000	18,500	42,500
Drug costs (adj for 12 months)	62,000	76,000	(14,000)
Subtotal	$171,800	$110,000	$61,800
NET BENEFITS			$21,800
RETURN ON INVESTMENT			14.16%

* from perspective of a managed care organization
† Control costs were based on 300 patients @ 4 visits/year/patient @ $60 per office visit. Clinic costs are based on 300 patients per year and one annual assessment by a physician at $30.

Formulary/Source: L. Basskin, PharmD

■ What are the therapeutic goals (patient outcomes) of the institution with respect to the specialty clinic? (See Exhibit 1 for a list of possible therapeutic [and nontherapeutic] objectives.)

■ What are the financial expectations and limitations imposed on the clinic by the institution, those who will pay for clinic services, and the clinic's direct competition?

■ What are the particular needs of the physicians or institution that refer patients to the clinic and the patients who attend the clinic?

■ Which health care professionals (and how many of them) will be needed to carry out these services? Do these people have the necessary skills or will additional training be required?

■ What potential conflicts will be created between traditional health care allies (e.g., pharmacists, nurses, hospital, specialists, family practice physicians) as a result of the development of the clinic? Does one party gain revenue or patients at the expense of another?

■ How, and how often, will the clinic be evaluated on its ability to meet therapeutic and economic goals? Are there specific dates and numerical goals for the clinic?

APPLICATION OF THE PE APPROACH

The methodology required to resolve this reader's problem is the same as that required to solve other pharmacoeconomic problems. After the services have been selected, one needs to plan how the analysis will be performed (and after what period of time) so that the appropriate data will be collected. The steps one could follow to determine the cost effectiveness of the clinic are as follows:

Prior to starting the clinic:

1. List the specific goals of the clinic.

2. List the specific objectives that need to be satisfied to accomplish the goal(s). These will be the basis for evaluating the "effectiveness" of the clinic.

3. For each objective, list the outcomes that will be measured to determine the "extent" of effectiveness.

4. Develop a data collection method to accumulate relevant outcome and cost data for each patient or patient group to be followed.

5. Select interventions that will likely result in the objectives being met.

After the time period for evaluation has occurred:

1. Compare the results of the clinic-treated patients with those of a control group. There are three common types of control groups, each of which is appropriate for different scenarios. One method is to compare the results before and after the intervention using the same group of patients. Another method is to compare the average results of clinic-treated patients with the average results of a group of patients with similar characteristics who were not monitored at the clinic. Finally, a third method is to "match" each patient seen at the clinic with a nonclinic patient who has similar characteristics (e.g., disease state, age, sex, concurrent medications). The results from each clinic patient are then compared with the results obtained from each matched control patient.

2. Determine the actual costs of establishing and operating the clinic (e.g., renovations, supplies, and salaries) over the time frame being evaluated.

3. Use a technique such as cost-benefit analysis or cost-effectiveness analysis to determine (a) if the clinic is cost effective (e.g., costs exceed benefits) and/or (b) if the measure of cost effectiveness (e.g., dollars per life saved) is acceptable compared with alternative uses of the available funds.

PROCESS FOR DETERMINING THE COST EFFECTIVENESS OF AN ANTICOAGULATION CLINIC

Let's consider our reader's problem and attempt to determine if an anticoagulation clinic is cost effective. The first step is to consider the reasons why a

■ TABLE 2 ■ COST-EFFECTIVENESS RATIO FOR CONTROL GROUP AND SPECIALTY CLINIC

Step 1: Compute cost-effectiveness ratio (CER) and marginal cost effectiveness

	Control group	Clinic group
Total monitoring cost (from table 1)	$114,000	$154,000
Costs per patient (300 patients)	$380	$513
Average no. of months of INR within target range (after adjusting for patients seen < 1 year)*	7.5 mo	9.4 mo
Cost-effectiveness ratio	$51/mo	$55/mo
Incremental cost per clinic-treated patient per month when INR was within target range†		**$70**

Step 2: Determine if marginal cost is a "fair" price to pay

Health care costs for inadequate anticoagulation (from table 1)	$171,800	$110,000
Costs per patient (300 patients)	$573	$367
No. of months that target INR was not met‡	4.5 mo	2.6 mo
Costs per patient per month that INR was not within target range	$127	$141

* calculated as 12 – the number of months the INR was outside the target range of 2.0 to 3.0.
† calculated as [(cost per patient in control group – cost per patient in clinic group) ÷ (months of INR within target range in control group – months of INR within target range in clinic-treated group)]
‡ calculated as 12 – the number of months the INR was within the target range of 2.0 to 3.0.

*Formulary/*Source: L. Basskin, PharmD

clinic might be useful and what goals it might accomplish.

From a therapeutic standpoint, the goal of anticoagulation therapy is to prevent clotting disorders (such as stroke or pulmonary embolism) without excess bleeding. Based on a review of the literature and clinical experience, we'll assume that if a patient's International Normalized Ratio (INR) is in the prescribed range of 2.0 to 3.0, the proper balance has been struck between the risks and benefits of the drug.

In establishing the appropriate measure(s) of effectiveness for the anticoagulation clinic, we'll need to consider two factors: the perspective of the analysis (i.e., will costs and benefits be measured from the perspective of the patient, the institution, or its employees) and the selection of therapeutic and/or nontherapeutic outcomes or goals relevant to that perspective.

An example of a nontherapeutic goal specific to an anticoagulation clinic might be to reduce the cost of monitoring warfarin therapy by substituting less expensive health care professionals for physicians without a loss of effectiveness.

Some examples of therapeutic goals specific to an anticoagulation clinic might include educating patients about warfarin therapy in an effort to improve patient compliance, or avoiding hospital admissions due to excess or insufficient anticoagulation (based on the patient's INR) by making dose adjustments in response to lab values.

For this study, our primary goal will be to reduce patients' total health care costs related to anticoagulation. A secondary goal will be to determine if the specialty clinic is superior to an individual physician management approach in keeping patients' INRs within the target range of 2.0 to 3.0. Our measure of both costs and effectiveness will take place after 1 year. We'll use the perspective of the HMO, which is responsible for paying all patient health care costs.

To measure the benefits (health care costs saved), we'll compare the costs of treating both clinic and control patients over a 1-year time period. These will include the costs of drug therapy, physician assessments, lab work, and hospital admissions for either excessive bleeding or the effects of under anticoagulation (deep venous thrombosis [DVT], thrombotic stroke, or pulmonary embolism). I have excluded outcomes that can't easily be converted into dollars, such as improvements in the patient's quality of life.

There are several ways to evaluate our second goal—the ability of the clinic to keep the patients' INRs within the target range. Since the goal is to maintain the INRs within the target range, it wouldn't be appropriate to measure the number of prothrombin time (PT) tests carried out or even the number or percentage of PT tests within the therapeutic range, as these can be manipulated simply by ordering more or fewer tests. Instead, we'll choose the number of months that the INRs were within the target range.

The results will be influenced by the degree of patient compliance with the therapeutic regimen, attendance at scheduled appointments, and avoidance or anticipation of drug interactions with warfarin. To achieve our desired results, we'll need to:

■ Review and keep track of concurrent medications, making recommendations to change dosing regimens as necessary.

■ Utilize a proven protocol for adjusting warfarin doses based on INR results, and therefore limit variability in recommendations between different people working in the clinic.

■ Develop a patient reminder system to ensure the patient returns to the clinic as often as needed.

■ Develop a plan for patient education to ensure the patient understands his/her medication regimen and the importance of complying with it.

To carry out our objectives, we'll need a clinic administrator, a full-time nurse, and a full-time pharmacist. We'll need to be tied into the HMO's computerized patient records, and we'll need furniture, computers, and an INR monitoring device. The costs of operating the clinic can easily be determined by obtaining quotes (or invoices) for equipment and renovations, using actual rent (or a fair value if space was donated by the HMO), and calculating the actual salary and benefits paid to staff and the acquisition plus dispensing costs for drugs. Assuming the HMO does not employ the physician, the cost will be the actual charge by the physician to the HMO for the patient visit. For monitoring costs, we'll use the actual cost of each blood test plus the cost of the equipment. For the control group, we'll use the marginal cost of a PT test as determined by the HMO accounting office.

For a control group, we'll use a group of similar patients seen at the HMO in the preceding year. We'll collect the same information for this group as will be collected for clinic-treated patients in the ensuing year.

Finally, we'll have to use two different techniques to determine cost effectiveness. With regard to the health care costs, we'll use cost-benefit analysis, in which the costs of the program will be subtracted from the benefits. This will be done to ensure that the benefits of the specialty clinic (health care costs saved) are greater than the sum of the costs to organize and run the clinic plus the health care costs of the clinic's patients.

With respect to the number of months in the target range, we'll use cost-effectiveness analysis to determine if the cost per month of clinic-monitored anticoagulation is less than the cost for monitoring conducted by each patient's personal physician. If patients had been seen by the clinic for less than 1 year, we'll extrapolate our results to 1 year (i.e., as if they had been seen at the clinic for the whole year).

RESULTS

In table 1, I've calculated the total costs and benefits to the HMO of establishing an anticoagulation clinic based on seeing 300 patients in the first year as opposed to having the PTs of 300 patients checked by their individual physician at each physician's office. For clinic costs, I included both renovation and yearly operating costs, which includes an annual assessment by a physician. (The HMO pays the physician $30 for this visit rather than $60 per patient per visit for a more traditional patient "office visit.")

For control patients, the lab charges the HMO $35 for each PT test. The cost for the clinic to perform the PT test, including a share of the cost of the initial equipment, is $10. The clinic would see the patient four times a year and report the results and recommendations to the physician.

The total costs of *operating* the clinic ($154,000) exceed the costs of the control group ($114,000) by $40,000. However, the benefit or decrease in health care costs in the clinic group compared with the control group was $61,800. Therefore the net benefits from operating the clinic (costs less benefits) were $21,800. The return on investment (net benefits divided by costs) was 14.2% on costs of $154,000. While the benefits did exceed the costs, administration would still have to decide if the 14.2% rate of return was satisfactory relative to its cost of borrowing to fund this clinic, or relative to the return on investment that could be generated from the funding of other projects within the HMO.

In table 2, the cost-effectiveness ratio (CER) was calculated for the clinic and control groups. It was based on the costs associated with operating the clinic, warfarin monitoring costs, and the average number of months in which the INR was in the target range of 2.0 to 3.0. The CER was $51/patient/target month in the control group and $55/patient/target month in the clinic group. However, since the clinic was more effective in maintaining patients' INRs within the target range (9.4 months vs 7.5 months for the control group) but costs were higher per patient ($513 vs $380 control), we need to determine the extra cost per month of using the clinic to obtain INRs in the target. When calculated, the incremental marginal cost per clinic-treated patient per month in which the INR was within the target range was $70.

Is $70 a reasonable price to pay per patient? The answer depends on the amount of benefits that result from each month gained by having patients' INRs within the target range.

In table 2, I've determined that the average health care costs of inadequate anticoagulation per patient were $573 and $367 for control- and clinic-treated patients, respectively. If we calculate the number of months that the target INR was met, we can determine an approximate cost of health care for each month that the target INR was not met. This equals $127 and $141 for the control- and clinic-treated patients, respectively.

Since the marginal cost per month per clinic-treated patient ($70) is less than the monthly per patient health care costs associated with INRs that fall outside the target range, it is cost effective to open the clinic and spend the $513-per-patient clinic cost since the benefit (i.e., avoidance of the health care costs per patient per month that the INRs are not within the target range) exceeds the costs (i.e., the marginal cost per clinic-treated patient per month that the INRs are within the target range). The cost advantage of opening the clinic holds true when calculating the results using either cost-benefit analysis and net benefits as the mathematical approach or cost-effectiveness analysis and number of months of maintaining target INRs.

Of course, neither of these analyses assumes that the clinic gains extra revenue since (assuming the patient has no copay) the HMO gains no extra revenue for each test or procedure performed. If the perspective of this analysis had been that of a traditional medical institution, such as a hospital, one might want to consider the extra revenue gained if the clinic is able to bill and recover the cost of these services through a third-party payer or from the patient.

Using decision analysis to solve pharmacoeconomic problems

Learning Objectives:

After reading this chapter, one should be able to:

1. Construct a decision tree for a given therapeutic problem which incorporates alternative outcomes, probabilities of occurrence and related costs of treatment.

2. Determine the average net costs or net benefits of any particular outcome by "folding back" the decision tree.

3. List the limitations of, and necessary conditions for, decision analysis.

Dr. Basskin,

I was reading a recent pharmacoeconomic study that used a technique called decision analysis. What is it and how does it differ from some of the other models you've described in previous columns?

Dr. RB
Magog, Quebec

Decision analysis is just another technique or tool to assist in selecting the most cost-effective therapy, drug regimen, or care pathway. You can use it to evaluate different alternatives when the costs (or costs net of benefits) differ *and* when there is uncertainty associated with the likelihood of an event occurring or a goal being achieved. It's a way of both improving quantitative aspects of the analysis while allowing you to visualize all alternatives and outcomes.

Decision analysis can be used with any of the existing pharmacoeconomic models, such as cost-benefit analysis, cost-minimization analysis, or cost-effectiveness analysis. The key difference between decision analysis and other pharmacoeconomic tools is that decision analysis takes into account the probabilities of an event occurring or a goal being achieved. Thus, the total cost of any alternative is the sum of each individual cost component multiplied by the respective probabilities that the costs of those components will be incurred.

STEPS FOR CONDUCTING DECISION ANALYSIS

To conduct decision analysis, you'll need to follow these steps:

1. Identify the therapeutic or medical problem.

2. Define (a) the perspective, (b) the patient population, and (c) the relevant time frame for gathering costs and assessing outcomes.

3. Specify the *primary goal(s)* for each decision alternative. A primary goal

EXHIBIT 1

Definition of terms

The terminology used in decision analysis can be confusing. The following are brief definitions of terms used in this chapter. Other authors may define these terms in equally acceptable ways.

Alternative: Two or more therapeutic options—e.g., different drugs—designed to solve a medical problem and accomplish the primary goal.

Primary goal: A positive therapeutic endpoint. What one would traditionally consider the main measurement of effectiveness of an alternative.

Secondary event: An undesirable occurrence—e.g., side effect—associated with a specific therapeutic alternative.

Outcome: The result achieved when one combines a specific alternative with its primary goal and secondary events. Each alternative can result in several outcomes depending on the number of possible combinations of secondary events. Some authors refer to these as different "pathways".

usually consists of an easily identifiable and clinically significant desirable therapeutic outcome that relates to the medical or therapeutic problem. For instance, a primary goal could be a cure, a life saved, or a defined improvement in a chronic disease (such as improvement in blood pressure for someone with hypertension, or reduction in the incidence of myocardial infarction for someone with coronary artery disease). It could also be prevention of an acute exacerbation of an existing disease state.

4. List the therapeutic *alternatives* under consideration that, with varying degrees of success, could solve the problem by allowing achievement of the primary goal. For example, amoxicillin versus trimethoprim/sulfamethoxazole for treatment of otitis media.

5. Specify significant *secondary events* that are additional but not unexpected complications or results of commencing drug therapy. In a decision tree, a "branch" is added for each significant secondary event. Examples of secondary events include drug toxicity, noncompliance with a drug regimen, and the need for second- or third-line options when primary therapy fails.

6. Assess the probability of occurrences of both primary goals and secondary events. First, assess the ability of each therapeutic alternative to achieve the primary goal. This can be done through direct observation or measurement of the effectiveness of the alternative in your institution or from a review of the primary literature (ie, from randomized clinical trials). Try to select a randomized clinical trial that assesses the efficacy of a particular therapy at achieving the primary goal in a patient population similar to that of your institution.

Probabilities of secondary events, such as toxicities or side effects, can usually be obtained from a reference source such as *Facts and Comparisons, AHFS Drug Information*, or even the package insert. I prefer not to rely on a single randomized clinical trial for toxicity probabilities, since significant side effects are often not discovered until after the drug is on the market and problems are reported to the manufacturer and the FDA.

7. Determine the costs of each alternative and of each secondary event. The method of determining costs of each alternative and events is the same as has been described in previous columns on this topic. For each alternative and events, (a) list the relevant cost components (e.g., lab tests, physician visits, clinic visits, facility usage [length of stay] costs, and drugs) from the selected perspective, (b) the expected rate of occurrence for each component, and (c) the cost (in dollars) of that component.

8. Draw the decision tree showing the alternatives, events, costs, and probabilities.

9. Use the technique described in this article to determine the total cost of each decision alternative.

SIMPLE EXAMPLES USING A DECISION ANALYSIS APPROACH

Suppose an institution is evaluating two drugs for pain, with a goal of recommending the most cost-effective agent (from the institution's perspective) for general use among its patients. The patient population is all hospitalized, nonsurgical, noncancer patients who require treatment for mild to moderate pain.

The two drugs under consideration are codeine and ibuprofen. For simplicity sake, we'll assume that both drugs are equally effective (100%) at relieving mild to moderate pain (the desirable primary goal) when dosed correctly.

We'll use decision analysis to select the least expensive alternative considering (a) the cost of the drug and (b) the costs of the relevant toxicities or side effects (secondary events) associated with each agent. The time frame is the expected 10-day course of therapy required.

We'll assume a 10-day supply of codeine costs the institution $10. Of all the patients who ingest codeine, about 20% will develop serious pruritus and require diphenhydramine, which costs $10. Therefore, the cost of treating any one patient could range from $10 (codeine alone) to $20, depending on the patient's reaction to the drug.

The institution, however, needs to know the cost of treating its entire population (and the average cost of treating a patient) to decide if codeine is less costly than another equally effective agent. If 100 patients were treated, the total cost of care would be $1,000 (100 × $10) for the narcotic, plus $200 (20 patients [100 × 20%] × $10) for the 20% incidence of pruritus, for a total of $1,200 for the 100 patients, or $12 per patient. Let's call what we've just described the *average cost method*.

This same problem could be solved using decision analysis. A simple decision tree for this problem is shown in figure 1. On the tree, the first square—or choice node—designates a decision that must be made, and the circle—or chance node represents the possible results that could occur from making the decision. Note that the sum of the probabilities of all nodes must equal 1.00 (100%).

The costs associated with each branch of the decision tree are calculated in

Figure 1

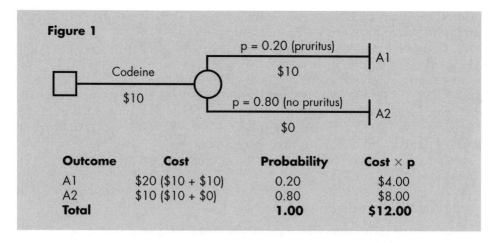

Outcome	Cost	Probability	Cost × p
A1	$20 ($10 + $10)	0.20	$4.00
A2	$10 ($10 + $0)	0.80	$8.00
Total		**1.00**	**$12.00**

the table beneath the figure. The total costs associated with any outcome are determined by following the outcome backwards to the start of the tree, adding up all costs incurred at each step from the right side of the tree to the left side. As can be seen in the figure, the overall cost of a given alternative is the sum of the cost of each outcome multiplied by the combined probability of each goal or event occurring.

We've now shown that the same $12 average cost determined using the average cost method can be derived using decision analysis. Therefore, for future discussion, we'll use the method of multiplying the cost by the probability to determine the average cost for the population.

Let's make the same example more complicated. Assume there is also a 10% chance of an anaphylactic reaction. When it occurs, the costs of a day's hospital stay ($700), a physician visit ($200), lab tests ($75), and drugs ($25) total $1,000.

In this example, there are two independent events that could occur (pruritus or anaphylaxis) and four possible outcomes that could occur: both toxicities (pruritus and anaphylaxis) (A1), pruritus only (A2), anaphylaxis only (A3), and neither event (A4). To visualize this decision tree, see figure 2. The average cost for each outcome that could occur is calculated by multiplying the total costs incurred to reach the outcome by the combined probability of the outcome occurring.

For example, consider outcome A1 in figure 2. For a patient whose pain management therapy follows this pathway, the total costs incurred would be $1,020 ($10 for initial therapy plus $10 for treatment of pruritus plus $1,000 to treat anaphylaxis). However, the combined probability of this pathway occurring is 2%, or 0.02 (20% risk of pruritus × 10% risk of anaphylaxis). This pathway adds $20.40 to the average cost per patient for the population (total cost incurred [$1,020] multiplied by the combined probability of all goals and events in the pathway occurring [0.02]). (For more discussion on calculating the combined probability when more than one independent event occurs, see Exhibit 2, "Probabilities: Moving from clinical trials to decision analysis.") Thus, adding anaphylaxis as a secondary event increased the average cost of therapy for the population from $12 (in figure 1) to $112 (in figure 2).

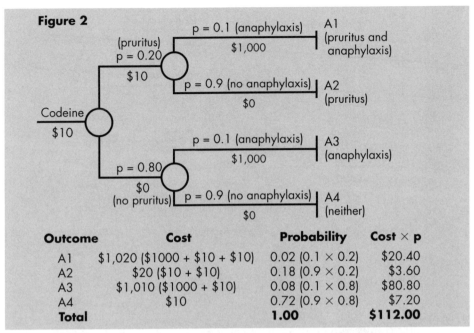

Figure 2

Outcome	Cost	Probability	Cost × p
A1	$1,020 ($1000 + $10 + $10)	0.02 (0.1 × 0.2)	$20.40
A2	$20 ($10 + $10)	0.18 (0.9 × 0.2)	$3.60
A3	$1,010 ($1000 + $10)	0.08 (0.1 × 0.8)	$80.80
A4	$10	0.72 (0.9 × 0.8)	$7.20
Total		**1.00**	**$112.00**

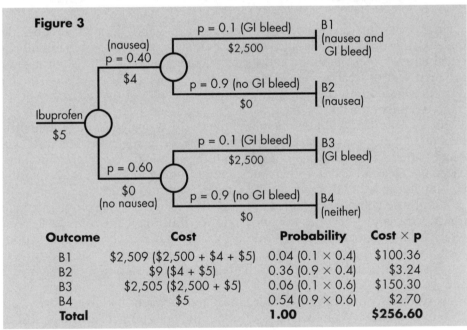

Figure 3

Outcome	Cost	Probability	Cost × p
B1	$2,509 ($2,500 + $4 + $5)	0.04 (0.1 × 0.4)	$100.36
B2	$9 ($4 + $5)	0.36 (0.9 × 0.4)	$3.24
B3	$2,505 ($2,500 + $5)	0.06 (0.1 × 0.6)	$150.30
B4	$5	0.54 (0.9 × 0.6)	$2.70
Total		**1.00**	**$256.60**

Finally, let's compare codeine with ibuprofen for pain, assuming that both drugs are equally effective when dosed appropriately. Ibuprofen will cost $5 for 10 days and is associated with nausea (occurs 40% of the time at a cost of $4.00 for treatment) and gastrointestinal (GI) bleeding (occurs 10% of the time at a cost of $2,500). See figure 3 for visualization of this decision tree.

Figure 4

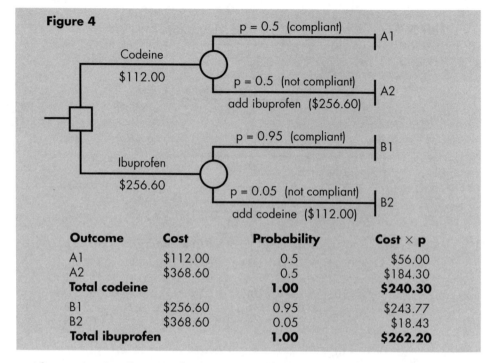

Outcome	Cost	Probability	Cost × p
A1	$112.00	0.5	$56.00
A2	$368.60	0.5	$184.30
Total codeine		**1.00**	**$240.30**
B1	$256.60	0.95	$243.77
B2	$368.60	0.05	$18.43
Total ibuprofen		**1.00**	**$262.20**

After reviewing the two decision trees (figures 2 and 3), one can conclude that codeine is actually a less expensive alternative than ibuprofen (assuming equal efficacy) despite ibuprofen's lower acquisition cost. This is because of the high cost of treating one of ibuprofen's toxicities—GI bleeding—which must be figured into the decision process, since 10% of the patients will require treatment for this event.

Finally, let's modify the problem and the decision analysis by assuming that patients are not equally compliant with their drug regimen. For instance, some patients may not fully comply with their codeine dosing regimen because they fear addiction to narcotics. Others taking ibuprofen may not fully comply because of GI discomfort associated with the drug.

With these compliance issues in mind, let's assign a 50% compliance rate for codeine and a 95% compliance rate for ibuprofen. Also, regardless of which drug was started, let's assume that the other drug is added if non-compliance is a problem with the first drug. The cost for the second drug is the cost determined previously in the respective decision tree (see figures 2 and 3).

As can be seen in figure 4, after taking into account the cost of adding a second drug due to compliance issues with the first drug, the average cost of treating a patient with codeine is still lower (although not by as much) than the average cost associated with treating a patient with ibuprofen ($262.20 vs $240.30).

OTHER HELPFUL TIPS

How far out do you need to extend your tree? Do you need to consider every possible secondary event, no matter how much it adds to the cost of a therapy? My rule of thumb in deciding if an additional branch or secondary event should be considered is that the average cost of an event (any branch) must be at least 5% of the total cost of therapy to have a significant impact, or affect the decision making process.

For example, assume that the total costs of a therapy under consideration are approximately $500 per year. If a drug has a toxicity cost of $1,000 and a 1% probability of occurrence, then the average cost in the population would be $10 ($1,000 × 0.01). Since $10 is less than $25—i.e., 5% of the total cost of therapy ($500 × 0.05)—I would not include this particular toxicity in my analysis.

Some readers might disagree with me on the grounds that, theoretically, all options and events should be considered if there is any chance that they could occur. My view, however, is that this should be a practical technique, not a theoretical one. Like everything else, the benefits obtained from using information (e.g., selecting a more cost-effective therapy) should be more than the costs of researching, locating information, and performing the calculations. I use the same criteria when deciding whether to order a lab test or to monitor a patient—it's only worth the time if the results of the test or monitoring would change my decision.

I offer one final tip on creating decision trees. As you are probably aware, various software manufacturers have developed decision analysis software that allows for easy preparation of trees and employment of sensitivity analysis (i.e., how would the results change if the cost or probability of an event were to change?). However, for those who want to save software costs, I recommend using a simple spreadsheet program, such as Excel or Lotus. Although it doesn't draw the tree for you, it still allows you to easily vary the costs and probabilities to determine how the results and conclusion could change.

KEY POINTS, LIMITATIONS

Let's review the important points and some of the limitations associated with the use of decision analysis.

■ Decision analysis is to be used in situations in which the primary goal can be eventually satisfied (i.e., an eventual cure or achievement of an acceptable quality of life). If not, the cost of failing to meet the primary goal must be able to be measured in dollars and treated as an additional cost of therapy.

For example, suppose the primary goal for treating diabetes mellitus was to eliminate the need for visits to a specialist. While an alternative therapy may be less than 100% effective at eliminating specialist visits, the costs of the partial failure (i.e., the cost of the extra visits) can be quantified and incorporated as the additional costs of that alternative. Unfortunately, quantification of primary goals that are less precise (e.g., improving quality of life with a better antidepressant therapy) is more difficult to perform.

■ The requirement for either equal or measurable goals can limit the usefulness of the results. For example, if one of the outcomes of one branch of

EXHIBIT 2

Probabilities: Moving from clinical trials to decision analysis

What is the relationship between the efficacy results of a randomized clinical trial and the probability numbers used in decision analysis? How can the results of a randomized clinical trial actually be used in decision analysis?

Results from randomized clinical trials relate to probabilities of occurrence in a very simple mathematical relationship. For instance, if in a treatment group of 500 patients with diabetes mellitus, 10 experience lactic acidosis and the sample is an accurate reflection of a given patient population, the probability that a member of the population would experience this adverse event would be 10 in 500, or 0.02 (2%).

In decision analysis, sometimes we need to take things one step further—i.e., we need to determine the combined probability of two independent events occurring. Let's consider angioedema and bone marrow suppression—two idiosyncratic toxicities associated with ACE inhibitors. If the probabilities of occurrence are 2% and 3%, respectively, what is the combined probability of both events occurring? If your patient population consists of 10,000 patients, 2% or 200 will develop angioedema, while 3% or 300 will develop bone marrow suppression. To determine how many patients would develop both angioedema *and* bone marrow suppression, consider the 200 patients with angioedema. They are a subset of the original population of 10,000 who should develop bone marrow suppression at the same 3% rate as the rest of the population (since the two events are independent, bone marrow suppression should occur at the same rate in all persons regardless of whether they also suffer from angioedema). Therefore 3% of the 200 patients, or a total of 6 patients, should suffer from both toxicities. This represents 0.06% (6/10,000) of the population. The same 0.06% could have been determined by multiplying 3% by 2%. In decision analysis, the latter technique is used to determine the combined probability of more than one independent event occurring for a group of patients.

a therapeutic alternative includes death or disability, when all other outcomes involve cures, assigning a dollar value to this outcome is virtually impossible.

■ The sum of probabilities after each decision choice node must equal 100%. Use this as a double check to make sure you have considered all possible results at each node.

■ Decision analysis can be used both for evaluating second- and third-line therapies or for determining the costs of treating toxicities or adverse events associated with drug therapy.

■ The model requires elaborate multiple-tier decision making. You have to continually evaluate what you would do if a therapy was not 100% effective or resulted in drug toxicities. What second- or third-line therapy would you use if the first-line therapy was unsuccessful? What are the costs of treating each of the side effects, and what is the likelihood of their occurrence?

■ The model determines what the average cost per alternative reached is for the population as a whole. That means that (a) the analysis doesn't necessarily apply to other patient populations, (b) what's best for the population may not be what's best for any individual patient, and (c) while the average cost for all patients combined will approach the final amount, the cost for an individual patient to achieve the desirable goals might follow the most expensive pathway.

■ In most of the articles which use decision analysis for problem solving, the authors generally assume that only *dollars* are a relevant factor in deciding which alternative should be selected. This ignores the fact that individual patients may prefer an alternative that is more expensive but is any or all of the following: less invasive, more palatable, easier to comply with, or taken for a shorter period of time. However, more sophisticated applications of this technique involve the use of patient or community preferences to "weight" individual pathways/outcome by "utility" factors.

Other patient preference issues generally not considered with decision analysis are postponing a treatment option until a later date or choosing an option that would result in less time away from work, an improved quality of life, or a higher rate of reimbursement from the insurance company. This is not a flaw unique to decision analysis; few pharmacoeconomic analysis tools are prepared from the perspective of the patient. Thus, these other "nondollar" but often emotionally charged issues are rarely taken into account.

While decision analysis has its limitations as a pharmacoeconomic tool, it has gained acceptance as a very useful way of trying to quantify several different variables. Those of you who read cost-effectiveness evaluations in medical and pharmacy journals will find that a familiarity with this technique will serve you well as it is rapidly becoming a method of choice in pharmacoeconomic analyses.

Assessing the impact of length of stay in a pharmacoeconomics analysis

Learning Objectives:

After reading this chapter, one should be able to:

1. List reasons why length-of-stay may be an imprecise measure of in-patient healthcare costs and/or effectiveness.

2. From a schedule of total historic costs, calculate the marginal hourly or daily cost of stay for an in-patient in an institution.

3. From a set of financial statements, calculate each of historic variable and fixed costs.

Dr. Basskin:

At a recent P & T Committee meeting I attended, there was a heated debate among the committee members about whether patients undergoing certain surgeries should stay in the hospital for 2 days or 3 days. Finally, one surgeon gave his best summation of the problem when he said, "I can't believe one extra day of stay for one more patient actually costs very much. We have already paid for the beds and nurses, so we probably make pure profit when we bill for one more day of stay. Besides, does it matter how long non-Medicare patients stay? Simply charge them for every minute of stay they're here. In fact, as I see it, by increasing their stay the hospital will profit. Besides, in my experience, the longer they stay, the less likely they are to return with complications from surgery."

I must confess to being confused. I thought reducing length of stay was always a goal of therapy, and that the hospital always saved costs as a result. Was I wrong?

JRB
Clinical Pharmacist
Louisville, KY

Actually, there's some truth to the viewpoints expressed by both the clinical pharmacist and the surgeon—sometimes extra length of stay (LOS) doesn't cost as much as we think, and sometimes the hospital makes a profit when its bill for services rendered is more than its cost to provide those services. Sometimes LOS is a good measure of cost savings, but it should be kept in mind that it doesn't mean it's the best measure to determine if one therapy is more effective than another.

In this chapter, I'll explore the use of LOS as a component of cost and mea-

EXHIBIT 1

What's wrong with using LOS as a measure of cost and/or effectiveness of therapy?

Using LOS assumes both that a shorter LOS is always positive, and that LOS is a good and fair measure of the success of one particular therapy or treatment. Below are some reasons why these assumptions are not always true:

■ If you shorten LOS by discharging a patient prematurely, you may be simply engaging in "cost shifting," passing the responsibilities for costs to the patient or even increasing the total health care cost to save your institution money in the short run. The total health care costs could increase if a premature discharge results in a longer recovery period, home health care, or time lost from work.

■ When you choose LOS as a measure, you assume that each area of the hospital costs the institution the same amount per day. The elements of cost (labor, supplies, and equipment) differ substantially in each of the main areas of a health care institution (e.g., emergency room, general medicine, surgical care, postoperative care, intensive care, maternity care).

■ Using LOS measured in days assumes that one extra minute of stay costs the same as an entire day. Moreover, if two patients occupy a bed on one day (presumably not at the same time), has the institution incurred costs equal to 1 or 2 days of stay?

■ The time of day at which discharge occurs is often completely arbitrary. For example, some physicians prefer to do all discharges in the morning during rounds. Some hospitals require outpatient counseling or physical therapy on the day of discharge before the patient is released. Some patients leave the hospital against medical advice, which can shorten the stay by hours at a time. Some physicians are very aware of the institution's billing policy and may seek to manipulate the discharge time to avoid having the patient charged for an extra day.

■ LOS can be increased even after patients have been cured. Sometimes, if the primary physician is unavailable (such as may happen on a weekend) the physician on call may not wish to discharge another physician's patient until the primary physician has seen the patient.

■ LOS might be increased if the patient is cured but still receiving intravenous therapy. Simply moving a patient to oral therapy may have resulted in a shorter LOS without any clinical significance.

■ LOS is often determined based on what a third-party payer is willing to pay. If a specific diagnosis related group, pathway, or protocol only covers 3 days in the hospital, the LOS may end up being 3 days regardless of the relative success or failure of one therapy over another.

Continued on next page

EXHIBIT 1 *(continued)*

Continued from previous page

■ The endpoints of some therapies are factors other than acute resolution of a disease (e.g., preventing readmissions or improving quality of life). In such cases, LOS is not an appropriate measure of effectiveness of therapy.

■ On occasion, a prolonged stay improves the outcome. For example, with some cancer treatments, the chance of decreased mortality or prolonged remission increases with more expensive and costly therapy (e.g., bone marrow transplantation over traditional chemotherapy for certain types of leukemia).

■ Decreasing the LOS can result in an adverse outcome if the result is a readmission for a complication that might have been avoided by bed rest or supervised observation (e.g., due to infection, a recurrent problem, or exacerbation of the acute problem that caused the initial admission).

■ For some patients, the cost of the extra day of stay might be billable and collectable and there is no financial advantage to trying to decrease LOS.

■ A given therapy might have been very successful, but LOS may increase because of a lower quality of care due to human error or inadequate staffing on the part of the hospital (e.g., inadequate nurse-to-patient ratio, insufficient number of technicians, or misread lab results).

■ A target LOS is usually an average value for a patient based on his or her specific disease state. LOS for an individual patient may be longer than "the average value" because of reasons unrelated to the therapy or the disease being treated. These include concurrent disease states, drug interaction as a result of concurrent drug therapy, nosocomial infections, the timing of or response to culture and sensitivities, or transfer to a step-down unit.

surement of effectiveness when performing a pharmacoeconomic analysis.

SHIFT IN PAYMENT PROCESS SHIFTS COST-SAVING FOCUS

Not too many years ago, physicians were encouraged to have their patients stay in the hospital longer, use more lab facilities, and not to worry about the cost of drugs. At that time, this made financial sense to the hospital, since those who paid the health care bill (patients or their insurers) usually paid 90% to 100% of the actual patient charges.

Today, of course, the situation is much different. Many employees are covered by a managed care or capitated agreement such that the physician, hospital/managed care organization/HMO, or even pharmacy collects a fixed monthly sum for all or a portion of the patient's medical care regardless of the actual costs of patient care. Many other patients have their health care administered by Medicare or a similar type of insurer. In this type of scenario,

TABLE 1 ALLOCATION OF HISTORIC COSTS

	Administrative, maintenance, and overhead	General medicine	Intensive care unit	Pharmacy	Total
Fixed costs					
Salaries	$850,000	$230,000	$75,000	$50,000	$1,205,000
Equipment	1,400,000	350,000	585,000	145,000	2,480,000
Education	2,000	13,000	6,000	10,000	31,000
Printing	14,000	3,000	2,000	4,000	23,000
Rent	750,000				750,000
Legal/Audit	24,000				24,000
Utilities	128,000				128,000
Total fixed costs	**$3,168,000**	**$596,000**	**$668,000**	**$209,000**	**$4,641,000**
Variable costs					
Salaries	$40,000	$2,100,000	$600,000	$500,000	$3,240,000
Repairs	2,000	23,000	14,000	13,000	52,000
Linens	129,000				129,000
Medical supplies		165,000	62,500	8,000	235,500
Drugs				1,200,000	1,200,000
Food services	258,000				258,000
Total	**$429,000**	**$2,288,000**	**$676,500**	**$1,721,000**	**$5,114,500**
Percentage sq. ft. of medical areas	N/A	75	10	15	100
Reallocation of variable AMO*	($429,000)	$321,750	$42,900	$64,350	$0
Total variable costs	**$0**	**$2,609,750**	**$719,400**	**$1,785,350**	**$5,114,500**

*AMO = Administrative, maintenance, and overhead costs

Formulary/Source: L. Basskin, PharmD

a fixed sum is paid to the hospital or health care provider for any one disease or diagnosis regardless of the LOS, number of lab tests ordered, number of drugs administered, quality of care rendered, or quality of life or outcome that results from the care.

Since revenue is effectively capped under these new reimbursement models, institutions are looking at each of the major cost components of patient care (e.g., drugs, labs, equipment usage, supplies, general care, and overhead) in an effort to reduce their costs and earn profits.

This shift in finances has affected the type of pharmacoeconomic analysis required. In older analyses, drug costs were the main or sole component evaluated. One therapy was determined to be more "cost effective" than another if the drug's costs were less expensive but the clinical outcomes were deemed equivalent. Today, drug costs are only one of the cost components considered. Other variables that need to be tracked and measured include number of admissions, duration of admission, number of physician visits, extra lab

TABLE 2 MARGINAL HOURLY COST	General medicine	Intensive care unit
Historic variable costs (HVC) (From table 1)	$2,609,750	$719,400
Number of patient-hours last year*	102,343	16,634
HVC per patient hour	$25.50	$43.25
Increase due to 10% inflation	$2.55	$4.33
Increase due to 5% decrease in productivity	$1.27	$2.17
Marginal hourly cost	$29.32	$49.75

*Equals number of patient-days x 24 hours/day

Formulary/Source: L. Basskin, PharmD

tests, drug therapy monitoring time, readmissions due to ineffective drug therapy or patient noncompliance, adding or eliminating the need for surgery, the cost of post-discharge care, and the quality and duration of life following completion of inpatient care.

However, studies that include all of these cost components can be expensive and time consuming to carry out, and impractical for individual institutions to conduct. As a middle ground, many investigators compare the costs of major care components (e.g., drugs, lab tests, and LOS) among different therapeutic regimens.

The largest of these components is the daily cost of care, referred to as length of stay (LOS). Each extra day of stay requires not only occupation of the bed, but use of other services including laundry, food, nursing, and cleaning. In addition, a prolonged stay results in the institution becoming responsible for a patient's "maintenance therapy"—i.e., drugs for illnesses unrelated to the admission that would have otherwise become the responsibility of the patient and routine lab tests that continue to be ordered daily.

There are, of course, legitimate clinical reasons to decrease LOS other than to save money. Having patients ambulate can decrease the risk of emboli forming. In addition, the risk of nosocomial infections decreases once patients are out of the inpatient setting.

It should be pointed out that LOS is not only used as a cost component. It is also used by some as a measure of effectiveness of therapy (under the assumption that those who are discharged earlier may have been cured faster). Therefore, we assume there is a clear correlation between LOS (and its relevant costs) and the "success" of any one therapy.

In my opinion, however, there are several problems associated with using LOS as an isolated measure of cost and/or effectiveness of therapy. For instance, a shorter LOS may not be the objective of the therapy and, in fact, may even be detrimental to good patient outcome, which is the therapeutic goal. Additionally, the actual cost of LOS may be very difficult to determine. Finally, there may be factors other than improved patient care that can result in a decreased LOS, and so LOS may not inversely correlate with effectiveness of therapy as one might have expected (see Exhibit 1 for a further discussion of this issue). Therefore, the goal should not be simply to reduce LOS; it should be to eliminated extra LOS that doesn't improve patient outcomes.

POPULAR WAYS OF CALCULATING LENGTH OF STAY

Once you've decided to use LOS as a cost component, how do you calculate it? Many published pharmacoeconomic analyses try to determine the cost of LOS using one of two overly simplistic methods.

The first method is to calculate daily LOS cost by multiplying patient charges by a cost-to-charge ratio (the ratio of total costs to total charges for the entire hospital). This method assumes that the patient charge has a logical basis of determination and is related to cost. However, patient charges are often determined based on "what the market will bear" and may have no logical relationship with the cost of a procedure or treatment. Moreover, the average ratio for the entire hospital and for all services assumes some services will be billed for much more than cost and some for much less.

The second simplistic method of approximation is to divide the total costs for a department by the total number of patients (or patient days) and use this as the cost of stay per day. However, this method suffers from two problems. First, it incorrectly assumes all costs are variable and that decreasing or increasing LOS by 1 day will save or cost the institution exactly the average cost per patient for that department. The second problem with this method is that it ignores the "administrative, maintenance, and overhead" (AMO) costs of running the institution not directly allocable to a department. The incorrect assumption is that all AMO costs are fixed for the institution and won't change in response to patient census. Some of the AMO costs (e.g., laundry, food, house cleaning) *do* vary in proportion to patient volume and are part of the cost of daily care.

In a proper pharmacoeconomic analysis, the goal is not to determine the total cost of a day's stay, but rather how many dollars would be spent or saved if the next patient stayed one more or one less day, respectively (marginal or incremental cost).

The *marginal cost* is defined as the *future variable costs* of patient care. *Historic variable costs* are determined by first subtracting fixed costs from total costs of care. (*Fixed costs* are those that do not change in response to changes in volume in the relevant time frame under consideration.) Future variable costs are calculated by adjusting the historic variable costs for expected changes in prices and productivity of the employees.

To illustrate this technique, let's use a simple example of a hospital that has four departments: administration, general medicine, intensive care, and pharmacy. Table 1 lists annual costs of a hypothetical institution. I've allocated costs between fixed and variable. About 90% of patient-related labor costs (e.g., in general medicine, ICU, and pharmacy) have been treated as variable costs though not all of the readers will agree with this large an allocation. While the number of nurses per shift does not change on the basis of one patient's LOS, it's my opinion that it does not take very much of a change in volume before nurses will have to be added or sent home. In this example, virtually all the direct health care labor will vary in response to volume throughout the 1-year time frame I've selected. The variable costs for administration were then allocated between departments on the basis of square footage.

In table 2, historical variable costs were then modified to reflect an expected increase in costs of 10% for next year. I've calculated the expected number of patients based on last year's census, but I've tried to consider expected changes due to the health care environment, contracts our institution has signed, and an expectation for a higher nurse-to-patient ratio negotiated in our last nurses' union contract, which takes effect next year. Finally, I have calculated the marginal cost of LOS per hour for both the general medicine wards and the ICU. It's these numbers that I intend to use in any future pharmacoeconomic analysis for this hypothetical institution in which I wish to track the costs of stay for different therapies.

MODIFY LOS, DON'T ABANDON IT

Despite the real and potential problems with measuring LOS, I don't recommend abandoning it as a cost component. Using cost component categories (i.e., LOS) and average hourly or daily costs is more practical and cost effective than tracking, measuring, and sorting costs of care for any individual patient. For the sake of ease of data collection, and to help make reasonable approximations, LOS is generally a good way of sorting and accumulating the costs of stay for an inpatient.

However, I am recommending that LOS not be used as a primary measure of effectiveness of therapy for the reasons I've discussed in Exhibit 1. I'm also going to recommend some changes in how we use and calculate LOS as a cost component, as follows:

1. LOS should be tracked and determined on an hourly basis (though in some areas, such as post-op, tracking is often done in minutes because many patients stay less than an hour).

2. The costs of LOS, for analytical purposes, need to be the marginal or incremental costs and not the average of both fixed and variable costs.

3. LOS costs need to include an allocation of the variable AMO costs of the institution. These costs should be allocated on the basis of square footage, number of staff, labor costs, or some other variable that reflects each department's share of AMO.

4. Both the hourly cost and LOS for any one patient need to be determined separately for each area in the hospital.

5. To eliminate the variation in LOS due to factors not being studied (i.e., confounding variables) try to keep track of those variables and group patients who have these variables in common. For example, since LOS is also affected by concurrent disease, keep track of patients in your study who have renal failure or are immunosuppressed.

6. Include as LOS the time resulting from readmissions that are likely due to an earlier problem that was not resolved. For example, you might include

LOS associated with readmissions for the same or related problem that occurs within 30 days of discharge.

7. When LOS is attributable to factors unrelated to the therapy being studied (e.g., seizures due to subtherapeutic drug levels but the patient was being treated for an infection with antibiotics), try to exclude the additional LOS from your analysis.

Using sensitivity analysis to improve your pharmacoeconomic analysis

Learning Objectives:

After reading this chapter, one should be able to:

1. List and define the reasons for uncertainty and multiple interpretations in a pharmacoeconomic analysis.

2. List seven different uses/techniques of sensitivity analysis in a pharmacoeconomic analysis.

3. Demonstrate the technique and uses of sensitivity analysis by evaluating the cost-effectiveness of a class of drugs throughout a range of amounts for each of cost and efficacy.

Dr. Basskin:

In several of your columns, you have indicated the need for making estimates and assumptions about variables when using different models. However, it seems that the models all require the assumption that each variable has only one fixed value. I'm concerned, though, that the use of an arbitrary "point" estimate of a specific cost component or measure of effectiveness is an oversimplification of the analysis. After all, someone else performing the same analysis could estimate a different input value or efficacy rate and reach results or a conclusion opposite to that obtained from my analysis. Are estimates really necessary? If so, how can I modify the analysis to ensure that more than one reasonable estimate is considered?

Dr. KM
P & T Committee Chair
Detroit, MI

Though we often analyze data retrospectively in a pharmacoeconomic (PE) analysis, the goal of most PE analyses is to predict the *future* costs and effectiveness of a given therapy. We do this by:

- observing the results obtained with the therapy and resources used,
- estimating the costs associated with different health care resources,
- evaluating the extent to which the conditions and costs will change in the future,
- modifying the results to reflect current or future conditions, and
- using a mathematical model to predict future costs and benefits.

The use of estimates, assumptions, and projections will always be required in any PE analysis because of the need to rely on historical data to predict fu-

EXHIBIT 1

Summary of uses of sensitivity analysis

■ To allow variance of cost and/or efficacy data through an entire range to see if the results and recommendations of a PE analysis would change.

■ To determine the threshold or break-even cost or rate; i.e., the point at which there is no difference in cost effectiveness between one drug and another.

■ To consider the extreme possible results of a PE analysis by evaluating the best or worst efficacy in combination with the best or worst cost of therapy.

■ To expand the scope of a PE analysis by including previously omitted costs and benefits, or to change the time frame of the costs and benefits being studied.

■ To vary the probabilities associated with the occurrence of positive outcomes or adverse outcomes such as death or drug toxicity.

■ To determine the effects on future costs—which are based on the predicted changes to historical data—by altering the assumptions on which the predictions are made (e.g., future census, changes in patterns of use of health care).

■ To allow alternative PE models (e.g., cost-effectiveness analysis versus cost-benefit analysis) to be employed to solve a PE problem, or to vary parts of the model (e.g., the interest rate used in discounting future costs and benefits into today's dollars).

ture costs, the lack of information needed for a complete analysis, the nature of certain PE techniques, the use of average values to predict future events, and the possibility of multiple plausible interpretations. Let's consider each of these separately.

1. Reliance on historical data. Assume you wanted to predict the future costs of adverse drug events (ADEs) in your institution. The cost of ADEs that occurred over a 12-month period can be summarized and sorted by prescriber, drug class, and suspected cause. For each drug or drug class, the number of ADEs, frequency of occurrence, average cost, and total cost to the institution can be determined. While these historical data are relied on to predict the future, the causes, calculations, or interpretations of these data may differ in the future and need to be adjusted or updated to improve the accuracy of future predictions. Factors that might change, and could, therefore, affect future ADE-related estimates, include the future census of the institution, the expected productivity of staff (e.g., how many patients will one nurse be expected to care for), the knowledge and identity of prescribers, the drugs being used, the effect of future patient compliance with drug therapy, the average age of the institution's population, and the cost of antidotes for drug overdoses.

2. Insufficient information. The effectiveness or costs of a study drug may not have been evaluated in the medical literature or at your own organization. Hence, estimates and predictions need to be made of both costs and effectiveness. In this case, other studies that provide some baseline information about the drug or disease under study need to be used but may need to be substantially modified if such information is insufficient in its provision of "hard" data.

3. Nature of certain PE techniques. Certain techniques require, by their nature, predictions about the future. For example, payments that extend over several years need to be discounted or converted into today's dollars. The discount rate chosen is a function of the future interest rate and the predicted rate of inflation.

4. Use of average values to predict future events. Even a flawless analysis of the costs and effectiveness of a given treatment is reported in terms of *average patient values.* Most PE analyses use these average values without considering the range of values obtained or the variance of the results about the mean. The extreme limits of the confidence interval represent possible results if the entire population were treated, and these should also be tested in PE evaluations by using sensitivity analysis. (Refer to Appendix II after Chapter 20 for a discussion of statistical terms such as means, variance, confidence intervals, and ranges.)

5. Multiple interpretations. It's quite likely that more than one interpretation of the results of a study, or of the definition of a certain cost category, is possible. In a PE analysis, one has to decide which interpretation is most appropriate, but one must also be prepared to perform the analysis using an alternative interpretation to determine if the results of the PE analysis would change.

SENSITIVITY ANALYSIS: WHAT IT IS, WAYS TO USE IT IN PE ANALYSES

Because of the five points discussed above, we use a technique called *sensitivity analysis* to determine if the use of alternative but plausible estimates, assumptions, or predictions would change the results of and recommendations from a PE analysis. Sensitivity analysis is a mathematical and analytical technique designed to improve the quality and usefulness of PE analyses. It can be used in conjunction with any of the PE models I've discussed in previous columns—e.g., cost-minimization, cost-effectiveness, cost-utility, cost-benefit, and decision analyses.

In sensitivity analysis, estimates of rates, costs, and benefits are made and then purposely changed to determine how the results would change. Generally, the technique involves holding all but one variable constant and calculating the new costs, outcomes, and overall cost effectiveness as this remaining variable is allowed to fluctuate between higher and lower values. The types of "rates" that could be varied include the rate at which disease states occur (prevalence), the success rate of a therapy (efficacy), and the likelihood of an event occurring (probability).

For example, a PE analysis may have initially shown that the cost effectiveness of a cardioselective beta blocker, such as metoprolol, for treating angina was superior to that of another beta blocker, propranolol. With sensitivity analysis, one could "replay" the model using the highest and lowest costs associated with different variables of administering each drug (e.g., different strengths, sustained-release dosage forms, oral versus IV administration, brand versus generic) to determine if metoprolol was always more cost effective than propranolol. If so, the results would be said to be *robust* or *insensitive* to changes in cost. The same technique could be applied to vary the efficacy of each drug at preventing the occurrence of angina, while holding the cost of each drug constant.

In more complicated applications of the model, both cost and efficacy would be allowed to vary simultaneously. For example, one could calculate the cost-effectiveness ratio of a drug by using the highest efficacy and lowest cost and comparing it with the highest cost and lowest efficacy—i.e., the best and worst cases. The values for the variables could be the extreme ranges of the confidence interval or any one of the values contained within the range. When a confidence interval is unavailable, one can adjust a variable both upward and then downward by an arbitrary amount, such as 10%, 25%, or 50%, to determine if the results remain insensitive to the changes.

Another way sensitivity analysis can be used is to determine at what cost or efficacy rate there is no advantage to selecting one therapy over another—i.e., the *break-even* or *threshold* cost or rate. This is accomplished by graphically or mathematically determining the rate or cost at which the net benefit (benefits less costs) or cost-effectiveness ratio (cost divided by efficacy) of a drug equals that of the drug it's being compared with.

For example, consider two drugs used for treatment of stroke—aspirin and ticlopidine. If the benefits (reduced health care costs) associated with use of these two drugs were $130,000 and $150,000, respectively, the cost of aspirin would have to be $20,000 less than that of ticlopidine for there to be no advantage for the use of ticlopidine. If 5 years of drug therapy were required, the cost difference between the drugs is $4,000 per year ($20,000/5 years) or about $11 per day. Therefore, if aspirin costs $1 per day, the maximum price to pay for ticlopidine—or the break-even point for ticlopidine to be equally cost effective to aspirin—would be $12 per day (since $12 − $1 = $11 break-even difference). However, if ticlopidine were associated with an average toxicity cost of $3 per day, the maximum price to pay for ticlopidine could not exceed $9 ($12 − $3) per day to be equally cost effective compared with aspirin.

Sensitivity analysis can also be used to vary both the costs and benefits as well as the probabilities of those costs and benefits occurring. In this case, the costs are multiplied by their likelihood of occurrence, and it is this likelihood that is allowed to vary, as if it were one of the variables. In the preceding example, if ticlopidine's toxicity costs were $3 per day, but the likelihood of them occurring was between 30% and 50%, using sensitivity analysis, the "cost" of toxicity could range from $0.90 ($3 × 30%) to $1.50 ($3 × 50%). The acquisition cost of ticlopidine itself could be as low as $10.50 per day ($12 less $1.50 for the toxicity-related costs that occurred in 50% of the patients) or as high as $11.10 ($12 less $0.90 for the toxicity-related costs that occurred in

30% of the patients) for the two drugs to be equally cost effective. If the percentage of occurrence is less than 100%, the "real average cost" of treating a toxicity ($3.00) is not used in the analysis. Notice how the use of probabilities for toxicity rates of less than 100% allows for higher threshold acquisition costs for ticlopidine over the $9 limit previously calculated.

Sensitivity analysis can also be used to identify areas in which additional research is needed to clarify the contribution of specific variables. For example, suppose a sensitivity analysis revealed that the results were insensitive to all changes in variables except a greater than 2% increase in the toxicity rate. In this case, it might be wise to explore the details of the toxicities, evaluating the incidence rates, costs of treatment, and risk factors to determine if there is a possibility of experiencing this higher toxicity rate in patients at your institution.

Another form of sensitivity analysis involves expanding the scope of the PE model to include previously omitted costs and benefits, such as those seen over a longer study. For example, suppose two thrombolytics, Q-PA and X-PA, were studied for the treatment of acute myocardial infarction (MI). The primary objective of the 1-year study was to decrease 30-day post-MI mortality. Costs considered were all those related to treating the patient at the hospital before discharge. A preliminary analysis showed that Q-PA's treatment costs were $3,000 less than X-PA's and Q-PA was associated with a 1% decrease in 30-day mortality. In this 30-day time frame, Q-PA was less expensive and more effective.

Sensitivity analysis can now be used to examine cost and efficacy results after 1 year rather than 30 days. It is now discovered that the difference in mortality has reversed itself and the extra 1% who survived with Q-PA subsequently died between 30 days and 1 year. Moreover, it is found that the patients treated with Q-PA who survived beyond the initial 30-day period had more admissions to the coronary care unit before they died. The health care costs in this group are now found to be an average of $5,000 higher than those of the X-PA group. In this 1-year time frame, X-PA was as effective and less expensive than Q-PA. Thus, by using sensitivity analysis, results were identified that might affect which thrombolytic would be the most cost effective for use at your institution.

PUTTING IT ALL TOGETHER

Now that we've tried a few different methods of employing sensitivity analysis, let's try an example in which we use several of the techniques in a progressive manner. We'll start with a simple example and gradually use more complex sensitivity analysis to see how the results change.

Assume you are evaluating the possible formulary addition of a new platelet inhibitor, which is indicated for use following coronary angioplasty. The drug reduces the likelihood that a follow-up surgical procedure (which would cost an extra $10,000) will be required. Published studies have shown the drug to be associated with an average efficacy rate of 10% (95% confidence interval of 5% to 15%). The cost of the drug is being negotiated with the manufacturer, and you have been asked for your recommendation

TABLE 1 COMPARISON OF COST AND BENEFIT COMBINATIONS FOR A PLATELET INHIBITOR	Best benefits, lowest cost	Lowest benefits, highest cost	Average benefits, average cost
Benefits	$1,500	$500	$1,000
Cost	$250	$2,250	$1,250
Net benefits (cost)	**$1,250**	**($1,750)**	**($250)**

Formulary/Source: L. Basskin, PharmD

as to the maximum price to pay.

In a cost-benefit analysis such as this, the costs of the drug (and its related toxicities, which we'll ignore for now) are subtracted from the benefits to determine if net benefits result. The benefits are defined as future health care costs saved.

The easiest method of calculating costs or benefits when the probability is less than 100% is to multiply the amount by the percentage likelihood of occurrence (refer to page 39 and Chapter 15 for more discussion of the technique and the logic behind it). In this case, the average benefit of drug therapy would be $1,000 ($10,000 for the cost of surgery avoided × the 10% average efficacy rate of the drug). Without employing sensitivity analysis, one might say the cost of the drug should not exceed $1,000 per course of therapy. However, let's consider the range of possible values. Based on the published literature, the true benefits could range from $500 ($10,000 × 5%) to $1,500 ($10,000 × 15%). In this case, one might want to make sure the drug cost did not exceed the minimum benefit of $500.

Let's modify this example still another way. Your institution is offered a price for the platelet inhibitor contingent on the number of vials purchased. The list price of the platelet inhibitor is $2,250, but depending on the volume purchased, the drug cost could be as low as $250. Table 1 shows the range of possible costs and benefits, as well as the average costs and benefits, associated with this offer. Using the maximum and minimum possible costs and the study confidence interval, you can see that the net results could be positive or negative.

Let's modify this example further with more information. It turns out that the average efficacy reported in the published study was with a patient population that had a history of multiple previous MIs, whereas much of your institution's population has never had a previous MI. You estimate there is a higher likelihood of success with the platelet inhibitor in your population and decide to weigh more heavily the higher efficacy with a higher probability of occurrence. You also find that you can predict the likelihood you'll pay either the lower or higher drug price after meeting with the cardiologists and estimating the number of angioplasties that will be performed and the likelihood that the platelet inhibitor will be used.

TABLE 2 COMPARISON OF NET BENEFITS FOR A PLATELET INHIBITOR WHERE PROBABILITY OF OCCURRENCE IS LESS THAN 100%			
	Best benefits, lowest cost	Lowest benefits, highest cost	Weighted total
Unadjusted benefits	$1,500	$500	
Probability of occurrence	70%	30%	100%
Adjusted benefits	**$1,050**	**$150**	**$1,200**
Unadjusted costs	$250	$2,250	
Probability of occurrence	80%	20%	100%
Adjusted costs	**$200**	**$450**	**$650**
Net benefits (cost)	**$850**	**($300)**	**$550**

Formulary/Source: L. Basskin, PharmD

Under this scheme, you'll compute one final value for each of the benefits, costs, and net benefits that are weighted by the respective probabilities of occurrence. Table 2 shows the new chart with probabilities incorporated throughout. You can see that the average results have changed from a net cost of $250 to a weighted net benefit of $550 using this form of sensitivity analysis.

You could also use this method to determine the break-even or threshold amounts. For example, using the expected benefits of $10,000 and a 10% efficacy rate, the price of the drug would have to average $1,000 ($10,000 × 10%) for you to break even. Alternatively, if the price of the drug was fixed at $2,000, the break-even amount in terms of benefits would have to be achievement of a 20% efficacy rate. Since the maximum efficacy reported in the literature was 15% (and a 20% rate is not obtainable), there would be no financial advantage to using this drug at that price.

CONCLUDING COMMENTS

As with all PE techniques, sensitivity analysis is one more tool that can be used to assist in making clinical and formulary decisions. It is never as simple as "picking the drug with the highest average net benefits." Here then are some provisos to keep in mind when using sensitivity analysis.

■ Make sure you have considered not just drug acquisition costs but the costs of drug preparation, delivery, and administration, as well as toxicity-related costs.

■ Make sure the outcome being evaluated and the PE model employed relate to the drug's therapeutic purpose. For example, if the purpose of a drug is to prolong life, the cost per life saved or cost per extra year of life should be the outcome measured using cost-effectiveness analysis.

■ Carefully consider the results of the sensitivity analysis when extreme values—rather than average values—are used for variables. It's possible for the average value to change very little in sensitivity analysis, but the results when using extreme values can show dramatic changes.

■ The decision or alternative selected based on the results of the sensitivity analysis will differ from institution to institution. Your final decision depends on available resources of the institution and its patients, the priority placed on a specific outcome, alternative uses for the funds by the institution, and whether the institution is responsible for all health care management and outcomes of its patients or only one aspect (such as inpatient care). A big question is whether the institution chooses to select drugs that offer potentially high returns and losses or is more conservative in its drug selection, foregoing the potentially higher returns in exchange for a decreased risk of significant losses.

Using cost-effectiveness analysis to evaluate therapeutic drug monitoring

Learning Objectives:

After reading this chapter, one should be able to:

1. Describe the goals of, and steps involved in, therapeutic drug monitoring (TDM).

2. Determine the cost, both total and per patient, of operating a TDM service.

3. Evaluate the benefits and cost-effectiveness of a TDM service by selecting and measuring appropriate outcomes.

Dr. Basskin:

The pharmacy department at our hospital has an extensive pharmacokinetic and drug monitoring service. When a drug is ordered that is on our "target list," pharmacists calculate empiric loading and maintenance doses and dosing recommendations, which are given to the physician. Pharmacists are authorized to monitor patients' signs and symptoms and serum drug concentrations and to make adjustments in the dosing regimen to meet predetermined goals of therapy. In an effort to focus more on outcomes rather than patient volume, we have decided to concentrate our efforts on selected drugs and patient populations. How can we determine which drugs and patients would benefit the most from such monitoring efforts? Also, what data should we collect and how should they be analyzed?

JD, PharmD
Pharmacy Director
North Carolina

One of the services clinical pharmacists provide is adjusting drug regimens in response to patient response and serum drug levels, better known as therapeutic drug monitoring (TDM). This TDM is typically conducted when selected drugs (e.g., lithium, digoxin, lidocaine, procainamide, gentamicin, warfarin, heparin, theophylline, phenytoin) are ordered for patients who meet one or more specific criteria involving age, renal function, or concurrent disease states or drug therapy.

Generally, TDM involves some or all of the following:

1. Developing goals for patient therapy, such as achievement of a target serum drug concentration (SDC). Other measurable goals are improvements in physical functioning tests, preventing reoccurrence of a disease, and preventing or providing relief from acute exacerbations of a chronic disease.

EXHIBIT 1

When should therapeutic drug monitoring (TDM) be considered, and what drugs are best suited to TDM?

Generally, drugs that warrant therapeutic drug monitoring (TDM) are those that have "narrow therapeutic windows" (i.e., relatively small dose adjustments can result in an SDC outside the therapeutic window or in a increase in the risk of toxicities). The window is based on statistical averages that usually include 95% of the people for whom the drug is effective but not toxic. There will always be 5% of the population for whom a "subtherapeutic SDC" is still efficacious, or who show signs of toxicity before a therapeutic level is reached, or who may require an SDC higher than the usual before either toxicity or effectiveness is reached, or for whom the actual window is smaller or larger than the average. Other conditions for which TDM may be recommended include the following:

■ for a drug with an unusual or high degree of interpatient variability in its pattern of absorption, distribution, or elimination resulting in difficult to predict SDCs.

■ when there is a strong correlation between the drug's dosing regimen, effectiveness, toxicities, and SDC.

■ when there are readily available laboratory tests that allow for timely, periodic monitoring of the SDC.

■ when the toxicities of the drug are generally predictable and avoidable with SDCs below a certain level.

■ when the effect of different patient parameters on the SDC (such as renal function, protein binding, weight, age, concomitant drug use) have been previously determined, can be reasonably estimated for any patient, and can be used in a mathematical manner to adjust the dosage regimen of the drug in question.

■ when the drug toxicities are potentially life-threatening.

■ when the desired outcomes are not immediately apparent from observation alone. In such a case, the SDC level may be the first clue that the drug is at a subtherapeutic level. For example, the gradual deterioration of cardiac output for a patient on a subtherapeutic levels of digoxin or gradual worsening of pulmonary function tests for an asthmatic patient on subtherapeutic level of theophylline could be detected earlier with TDM.

■ when the drug is associated with toxicities (such as arrhythmias, kidney damage, osteoporosis, cataracts, changes to blood pressure, loss of hearing, worsening of diabetes, liver damage, heart failure) that either do not exhibit readily observable signs and symptoms or may not be evident until the damage is irreversible. Accordingly, it is important to obtain the SDC and ensure it is below the toxic level.

Continued on next page

EXHIBIT 1 *(continued)*

Continued from previous page

■ when drugs have likely and predictable interactions with other drugs in which the SDC can be dramatically affected. Classic examples of drugs that can increase or reduce other drugs' SDCs by inducing or inhibiting their metabolism include warfarin, erythromycin, ketoconazole, phenytoin, and cimetidine.

No guarantee of outcomes with TDM

To play devil's advocate, TDM is effective only if there is a strong correlation between TDM, SDC, dose adjustments, and the outcomes achieved. Consider the following reasons why TDM might fail even if the correlation between dose and SDC is strong.

■ When a dose adjustment is made to bring the SDC within the "therapeutic range," we assume that the adjustment was needed to cure the patient or prevent the occurrence of a toxicity. Since the range represents the average range for all patients in the population, there is no guarantee that the same outcome for any one patient might not have occurred even without a dose change.

■ Desirable outcomes, such as a cure of an infectious disease, may have occurred even if the drug had been discontinued. For example, gentamicin (a drug often subject to TDM) is usually added to a regimen for the treatment of gram-positive infections for synergistic purposes. Therefore, it is unclear if the addition of the drug, let alone achieving a certain SDC, was necessary.

■ Undesirable outcomes can occur even while the SDC is in the therapeutic range. There is no guarantee that adjustments to SDC will prevent poor outcomes from occurring.

■ Monitoring is done even when the relative risk of toxicity is low. For example, vancomycin was thought for years to be ototoxic and was subject to TDM in many institutions. More recently, this theory has been refuted in the medical literature.

2. Recommending empiric loading and maintenance dosage regimens based on the drug's absorption, distribution, and elimination as well as factors such as the patient's weight, body surface area, renal and hepatic function, immune status, and concurrent drug therapy.

3. Ordering and interpreting SDCs and making recommendations or adjustments to the drug's dosage regimen to meet the target SDC.

4. Observing the patient for signs and symptoms of toxicity, which might necessitate a recommendation to lower the dosage or provide less frequent dosing.

5. Monitoring the patient's clinical progress by ensuring that the drug level is not subtherapeutic.

With the background on TDM laid, let's examine this reader's questions:

How to identify the drugs and patient populations that would benefit the most from a TDM program, and what data are needed to perform a pharmacoeconomic (PE) analysis of the cost effectiveness of TDM programs?

EVALUATING TDM PROGRAMS

To answer these questions, one needs to look at the costs of a drug monitoring program for a patient population and compare them with the benefits or improved outcomes associated with the TDM program. A general outline of a plan to determine the costs and benefits might be the following:

1. Identify the outcome to avoid or obtain. The outcome selected is usually based on the purpose and side effects of the drug therapy.

2. Determine the benefits of such an outcome in dollars or in units of effectiveness.

3. Determine the types and quantity of health care resources or cost components (e.g., laboratory tests, drugs, labor) used in TDM.

4. Assign unit costs to each resource.

5. Study a randomized group of patients for whom TDM was not performed and compare the results with those in a group of patients for whom TDM was performed. In each case, measure the average cost of resources consumed and average record of effectiveness.

6. Use a PE model or technique to determine the cost effectiveness of the service by itself or in comparison with another service.

It is important to note that the parameters usually measured in TDM (such as SDC) are not true outcome measures but only indicators of whether the proper amount of drug is being administered. Accordingly, one should make sure that there is a strong correlation between the SDC and the likelihood of either an improvement in patient outcomes or decrease in toxicities experienced. Even if the correlation is strong, there are other reasons why therapy may fail despite achieving the SDC. These other factors are called "confounding variables" and need to be taken into account when evaluating the effectiveness of the TDM service. Some of these variables are the patient's age, gender, weight, concurrent medications, and immune status.

There are three different ways in which confounding variables can be accounted for (1) exclude patients with confounding variables from the study; (2) randomize all of the patients between study groups, which will hopefully lead to patients with similar mixes of characteristics in each group; (3) characterize, and then stratify, the patients by major differences in their demographic data into different subpopulations, and determine the outcomes for each different subpopulation.

What are the best data to collect? I have found three useful measurements of the effectiveness of a TDM program.

1. An accurate assessment of the duration of time (hours, days, or months, as appropriate) during which the patient's SDC is within the target range. The appropriate PE model to use would be cost effectiveness, measured as *dollars per unit of time.*

2. The inclusion of costs of all health care resources used. Such costs are easily obtained if the drug to be used is one that will be discontinued in a

relatively short, observable time period (e.g., IV antibiotics). With these types of drugs, any additional costs associated with complications would be incorporated into the PE analysis and *net costs or benefits, in dollars* would be evaluated using cost-benefit analysis.

3. Determination of the "event-free" rate. This is defined as the rate at which there were no incidents of therapeutic failure or drug toxicities that required intervention. This would be evaluated using cost-effectiveness analysis and expressed as *cost per event-free therapy*.

How to Evaluate Cost Effectiveness of a TDM

Let's perform a PE analysis on a drug subjected to TDM to determine if the service is cost effective. We'll look at IV lidocaine. Before performing a PE analysis, an understanding of the drug's therapeutic use, its range of minimally effective-to-toxic SDCs, and signs and symptoms of both positive outcomes and drug toxicities is needed.

Lidocaine is generally effective when administered intravenously as treatment (and occasionally as prophylaxis) for ventricular tachycardia (VT). It is given to patients following cardiac surgery, myocardial infarction, or other cardiac event whose rhythm, as shown on the electrocardiogram (EKG), demonstrates a high risk of deterioration into ventricular tachycardia.[1] These include brief runs of VT and the presence of multiple-shaped or excessive premature ventricular contractions (PVCs). Lidocaine suppresses these PVCs and, hence, reduces the risk of sudden cardiac death from VT or ventricular fibrillation (VF) in the period immediately following the surgery or infarction.[2,3]

Lidocaine is not without toxicities. In one published study,[3] 6.3% of patients (47 of 750) experienced adverse events attributed to IV lidocaine. In 12 of these 47 patients, the reactions were considered life-threatening and included respiratory distress, coma, grand mal seizures, heart block, cardiac arrest, and hypotension. Other less serious adverse reactions to lidocaine include drowsiness, fasciculations, numbness, hallucinations, slurring of speech, and severe agitation.[4]

Lidocaine is first administered as a series of loading doses, followed by a maintenance dose of 1 to 4 mg/minute. The goal is to keep the patient from progressing from simple PVCs to VT or VF, but without experiencing signs and symptoms of toxicity. A goal SDC of between 2 and 5 mg/l is often used as a guideline, though patients are continually monitored for the presence or absence of PVCs.[5]

There is a great deal of patient variability in the SDCs obtained from IV lidocaine. These may be due to variability in protein binding of the drug, the effect of lidocaine metabolites, and the effects of concomitant disease and drug therapies from patient to patient.[2]

To monitor the patient and make recommendations regarding loading and maintenance doses of lidocaine, one needs to know the patient's hepatic and renal function, actual and ideal body weight, goal SDC, signs of subtherapeutic levels, symptoms of toxicity, concurrent drug therapies (other drugs that inhibit the metabolism of lidocaine such as beta blockers or cimetidine),[2]

TABLE 1 COSTS AND EFFECTIVENESS OF A LIDOCAINE MONITORING SERVICE

	Control group n (%)	LMS group n (%)	Incremental difference n (%)
Number of patients:			
participated	45	49	4
survived	41 (91.11%)	46 (93.88%)	5 (2.77%)
toxicity free	34 (75.56%)	44 (89.80%)	10 (14.24%)
free from breakthrough arrhythmias	31 (68.89%)	37 (75.51%)	6 (6.62%)
Average number of dose decreases	2.6	1.5	− 1.1
dose increases	3.8	2.0	− 1.8
Average number of serum drug concentrations (SDCs)	2.0	3.5	1.5
Cost per SDC	$37.00	$37.00	$0.00
Total SDC cost	**$74.00**	**$129.50**	**$55.50**
Average pharmacist monitoring time/patient (min)*	0	65	65
Average pharmacist monitoring cost/patient*	$0.00	$32.50	$32.50
Total monitoring and SDC cost	**$74.00**	**$162.00**	**$88.00**

*In the control group, monitoring was conducted by physicians; in LMS group, monitoring was conducted by pharmacists based on a pharmacist salary cost of $30/hr or $.50/min

Formulary/Source: L. Basskin, PharmD

and extent of liver disease, myocardial infarction, or congestive heart failure (which can decrease the rate at which lidocaine is cleared from the body).[2]

A lidocaine TDM might include ordering and examining laboratory tests, EKGs, and rhythm strips, meeting with physicians, direct patient observation, measuring lidocaine SDCs at appropriate times (after dose changes), and recommending new dosage regimens based on desired SDCs in response to signs of subtherapeutic levels or lidocaine toxicity.

Case report. Consider the following scenario from an institution for whom I consulted that wanted to implement a lidocaine monitoring service (LMS) (actual results have been altered to demonstrate the analytical techniques more clearly).

Cardiologists at the institution traditionally dosed lidocaine for each patient using a prolonged, phased-in loading dose of 75 to 100 mg of lidocaine, followed by a maintenance infusion of 2 mg/min. Patients whose PVCs were not suppressed had their infusion dosage increased incrementally by 1 mg/min. Patients experiencing signs of toxicity had their dose lowered by 0.5 mg/min. Lidocaine SDCs were taken inconsistently.

TABLE 2 INCREMENTAL COST-EFFECTIVENESS CALCULATIONS FOR LIDOCAINE MONITORING SERVICE			
	Survival	**Toxicity-free therapy**	**Arrhythmia-free therapy**
Incremental costs (from table 1)	$88.00	$88.00	$88.00
Incremental rate of effectiveness	2.77%	14.24%	6.62%
Incremental cost per patient*	$3,177	$618	$1,329

Note: Costs included are only those that differed between the control group and the lidocaine monitoring service

* Incremental cost divided by incremental rate of effectiveness

Formulary/Source: L. Basskin, PharmD

The cardiologists were reluctant to use an LMS because the laboratory could not return SDC results within 24 hours. Also, there was no evidence that an LMS would produce outcomes better than could be achieved using their own method.

The pharmacy department wanted to implement an LMS for several reasons: lidocaine has a narrow therapeutic window (discussed in Exhibit 1), it needs individualized dosing because of interpatient variability in SDCs, and it has a complex loading-dose regimen.

The institution decided to implement an LMS using a pharmacokinetic computer program to determine the staggered series of loading doses and the empiric maintenance dose based on the patient's weight, hepatic function, cardiac output, and goal SDC. (Note to readers: These types of programs have been evaluated in the medical literature and found to be superior to physician estimates of the maintenance infusion necessary to reach the desired SDC.[6-8])

In addition, the laboratory procedure was refined so that SDC results would be returned within 8 hours. Patients were monitored twice daily. An SDC measurement was ordered after the first dose and daily thereafter, plus after each dosage change.

Evaluating the LMS outcomes. It was hypothesized the use of TDM would reduce the incidence of toxicities while ensuring that patient SDCs were kept above subtherapeutic values, which would result in fewer cases of unsuppressed PVCs and a lower incidence of sudden cardiac death.

To evaluate the program's outcomes, the institution collected data to answer several questions:

1. Did the LMS increase or decrease the number of maintenance doses needed and/or SDCs taken?

2. Were there fewer deaths from sudden cardiac death as a result of the LMS?

3. Were the "event-free" rates (i.e., the number of times during which neither

toxicity nor breakthrough ventricular arrhythmias occurred) lower with LMS?

Data were collected and summarized for 3 months from 94 patients with similar risk factors (e.g., no prior history of VF or VT and receiving no other antiarrhythmic agents).

Results (table 1) show that the LMS group achieved better clinical outcomes but used more health care resources than the control group. In terms of dose increases and decreases, the control group required more adjustments but had fewer SDCs measured. In the LMS group, pharmacists made dose adjustments based on SDCs and were instructed to measure SDCs after each dose change. Physicians in the control group, however, were more likely to have made dose changes in response to clinical outcomes rather than relying on and measuring SDCs.

The monitoring time was measured for both pharmacists and physicians; however, since *physician* costs were not paid directly by this institution, their costs were not included in this analysis. Accordingly, while we do not know from this study whether the use of an LMS increased or decreased physician monitoring time of lidocaine's effect and toxicities, we can hypothesize that fewer interventions with an LMS would decrease the physician's time required per patient.

Analyzing cost effectiveness. The next step is to determine the cost of obtaining the higher efficacy. Since the analysis is concerned with the extra costs to the institution associated with the LMS program, the total costs of lidocaine therapy do not need to be considered unless the costs (or health care resources consumed) differ between the LMS and control groups. In this case, the only difference between costs of the two groups is the number of SDCs measured and the cost of monitoring. The incremental cost of providing LMS is $88 per patient—$162 per patient for the LMS group compared with $74 per patient in the control group.

To determine the incremental cost-effectiveness ratios for the LMS (table 2), the incremental costs between the groups are divided by the incremental effectiveness rates. Results show that the cost-effectiveness ratios are $3,177, $618, and $1,329 for cost per life saved, toxicity-free therapy, and arrhythmia-free therapy, respectively.

Interpreting results. To interpret incremental cost-effectiveness ratios, imagine that 100 people were treated with the LMS. The additional costs would be $88 per patient or $8,800 for the entire group. Using the difference in efficacy rate for survival of 2.77%, the cost per life saved is $8,800 ÷ 2.77 (number of lives per 100), for an average cost of $3,177 per life saved.

The next step is for the institution's administration to decide if these amounts are reasonable to pay to save an extra life or for an extra course of therapy. There are three ways to make this comparison. The first is by looking at the amount and comparing it with the costs of other therapies designed to accomplish the same purpose. For example, some studies have found that an acceptable cost per life saved (e.g., using dialysis or antihyperlipidemic drugs) is $100,000. Using this comparator, an amount of $3,177 per life is a reasonable price to pay, and the LMS would be cost effective.

Another approach is to compare the cost per toxicity avoided with the cost to treat that toxicity. For example, the cost of $618 per toxicity avoided might be compared with a cost of $1,000 to treat that toxicity. If the costs of the intervention (i.e., the monitoring) are less than the costs of treating the toxicities, this would be a worthwhile investment, and the LMS would be deemed cost effective.

The last approach involves trying to rationalize the cost-effectiveness ratio by comparing it with a possible result. For example, it costs $1,329 to have an arrhythmia-free therapy, but what is the cost of an arrhythmia? If the "cost" of a death is the amount one would pay to avoid its occurrence, we can use the $100,000 mentioned above as a cost the health care institution would pay for treatment designed to prevent death. If the likelihood that the arrhythmia would progress to death is, say, 10%, then the "expected cost" of the death is 10% × $100,000 or $10,000 (see Chapter 15 on decision analysis for a further discussion of this technique). Since the expected cost of the arrhythmia, at $10,000, is more than the $1,329 required to prevent it with an LMS, the LMS would be cost effective and should be implemented.

We could use the technique of sensitivity analysis to explore different rates of occurrence to determine if there are limits to monitoring time or results, at which LMS would no longer be cost effective for any of the three parameters selected.

Finally, remember it is important to document what is done in TDM for several reasons:

■ It leaves a paper trail that can be followed by the other health care professionals who care for the patient after your shift.

■ It provides evidence of what you've done. This is essential when you want to justify the services rendered.

■ It provides a therapeutic and monitoring plan.

The kind of documentation necessary for a PE analysis differs from the typical "clinical" or "progress" notes. Data collected should enable you to evaluate both the cost and the effectiveness of a drug, surgical procedure, or therapeutic plan. To facilitate data collection, sort and gather data that are quantitative rather than descriptive or qualitative. Then use computerized spread sheets and databases to summarize the information.

REFERENCES

1. Herlitz J, Ekstrom L, Wennerblom B. "Lidocaine in out-of-hospital ventricular fibrillation. Does it improve survival?" Resuscitation 1997;33:199-205.
2. Pieper JA, Johnson KE. Lidocaine. In: Evans W, Schentag J, Jusko W, eds. Applied Pharmacokinetics, Principles of Therapeutic Drug Monitoring, 3rd ed. Vancouver, BC: Applied Therapeutics Inc, 1992.
3. Sawyer DR, Ludden TM, Crawford MH. "Continuous infusion of lidocaine in patients with cardiac arrhythmias." Arch Intern Med 1981;141:43-5.
4. Schuttler J, Bremer F, Hornchen U. "Pharmacotherapy of ventricular fibrillation: A prospective study in an emergency medical service." Anaesthesist 1991;40:172-9.
5. Hilleman DE, Mohiuddin SM, Mooss AN, et al. "Comparative pharmacodynamics of intravenous lidocaine in patients with acute and chronic ventricular arrhythmias." Ann Pharmacother 1992;26:763-7.
6. Beach CL, Farringer JA, Crawford MH, et al. "Clinical assessment of a two-compartment

Bayesian forecasting method for lidocaine." Ther Drug Monit 1988;10:74-9.

7. Vozeh SV, Berger M, Wenk M, et al. "Rapid prediction of individual dosage requirements for lidocaine." Clin Pharmacokinet 1984;9:354-63.

8. Vozeh SV, Uematsu T, Ritx R, et al. "Computer-assisted individualized lidocaine dosage: Clinical evaluation and comparison with physician performance." Am Heart J 1987;113:928-35.

Designing a user-friendly format for reporting an internal pharmacoeconomic analysis

Learning Objectives:

After reading this chapter, one should be able to:

1. List the ways in which a pharmacoeconomic or outcomes research report differs from a published pharmacoeconomic study.

2. Define the important parts of a pharmacoeconomic report based on the needs of the user of that report.

3. Explain the importance of disclosure of methodology versus selection of methodology in a pharmacoeconomic analysis.

Why are decision makers reluctant to use pharmacoeconomics (PE) and the results of published PE studies both in the formulary decision-making process and when deciding which drugs to include in clinical or disease state pathways? Maybe it's because many published PE studies fail to focus on clinically significant outcomes or use study parameters that are too restrictive (e.g., use of a study population that is unrealistic or inclusion of inappropriate comparator agents). Or, maybe it's because the PE models and techniques being used are too sophisticated for the intended user of these studies. My own opinion is that the biggest reason why PE information isn't being used is because the typical published PE study, in its existing form, does not meet the needs of decision makers who must use that information. The user often needs several PE studies evaluated, restated with relevant cost and efficacy information, and presented in a simple, summary format.

In this chapter, I'll share some insights into how to prepare an easily digestible and user-friendly PE report for presentation to drug decision makers.

WHAT IS A PE REPORT AND WHAT INFORMATION SHOULD IT CONTAIN?

A pharmacoeconomic (PE) report should provide the information needed to make a decision about what drug should be selected from among alternatives for treating a specific disease state or for inclusion on a formulary. It should be presented in a format that is concise, yet complete and should be understandable by health care professionals whose experience with PE is limited. It should summarize research results and contain specific recommendations. A PE report is a document that is requested by decision makers, such as a pathway team member or P & T Committee member, who are relying on the unbiased expertise of the report preparer.

The content of a PE report is different from that of a PE study (see table 1 for some of the key distinctions). In general, the PE report requires a comprehensive review of published or internal PE and efficacy data and other

TABLE 1	FACTORS THAT DISTINGUISH PERSPECTIVE AND/OR CONTENT OF A TYPICAL PE STUDY FROM A PE REPORT	
	PE study	**PE report**
Comparative agents	Few are used; rarely compares selected drugs to those outside the drug's chemical class	Compares all drugs in the same therapeutic class
Disease states evaluated	Usually one state, without concurrent problems or concurrent drugs	Considers multiple disease states and concurrent drugs
Costs of therapy	Generally considers the cost of the drug and treatment in an isolated problem	Considers health care system costs of switching from one drug to another
Integration of related PE analyses	May comment on other related PE analyses for comparative purposes	Must integrate related analyses for decision making
Primary emphasis and purpose of reporting results	Emphasis on PE technique and research design; should contain sufficient detail to allow for replication or modification of study in different settings	Emphasis on clarity of presentation and reasonableness of recommendations in unique health care setting
Objectivity of report	May reflect the bias of the sponsor or of funded investigators	Recommendations are based on objective measures of cost and effectiveness, with all relied-upon studies critically evaluated for potential bias
Goal of the analysis	Concerned with generating final numerical answer or ratio	Provides information to enable "judgment call" or interpretation of values or ratios to be made
Patient population	Usually uses a patient population with narrowly defined characteristics (i.e., efficacy)	Applies to the general population of the institution with its multiple concurrent drugs and diseases (i.e., effectiveness)

Formulary/Source: L. Basskin, PharmD

EXHIBIT 1

The importance of adequate disclosure of methodology

It has been 20 years since the first pharmacoeconomic (PE) study was published. Since that time, economists, academicians, and health care providers have been engaged in a lively debate about the appropriateness of different PE techniques. As a result, the definitions of what is "acceptable" PE methodology have been narrowed.

Unfortunately, the extent of standardization is not as far along as some would like us to believe. Commonly used words such as "cost," "effectiveness," or "discounting," can still have several different, and equally acceptable, meanings. In addition, there is no requirement to use any one method (such as cost-benefit or cost-effectiveness analysis) for any one type of PE problem. Some organizations have tried to encourage standardization of methodology by developing guidelines or principles. Others, such as the International Society for Pharmacoeconomics and Outcomes Research, have developed an extensive lexicon/glossary in an effort to gain a consensus on the meaning and applicability of certain PE phrases and words. While I applaud these efforts, I suggest that both PE analysts and users worry less about "correct methodology" and more about the adequacy of disclosure of the techniques and definitions used and on the assumptions made. I say this for the following reasons:

■ Since certain terms are widely misused in the literature, most users of PE information may have a different understanding of a term than that of the author of the PE study. Disclosure of the definition would, therefore, help reduce misinterpretation of the PE study's results or conclusions.

■ There are several equally acceptable PE methods that can be employed to solve a PE problem, depending, in part, on the needs of the user and the objectives of the author. By disclosing adequate information on the methods used, users of PE information will be able to better assess the methodology and will not automatically judge the study as "good" or "bad" simply on the basis of the PE technique selected.

■ Certain parts of a PE analysis involve the use of ranges or alternative input values. Disclosure of these input variables—such as the range used in sensitivity analysis, the interest rate used for discounting, the characteristics of the patient population studied, and the period of time over which the costs and benefits were gathered—is essential if the PE report preparer and end user or decision maker is to assess the usefulness and relevance of the PE study as it would apply to their own population.

■ Disclosure of assumptions and calculations allows users of the PE study to insert their own measures of cost and effectiveness, and then reperform the study to see how results and conclusion might change.

relevant literature about the use of a drug for multiple disease states in different populations. The report preparer then needs to evaluate the validity and usefulness of the data and studies, determine the costs of therapy from the perspective requested by the ultimate user (which may differ from that used in the PE studies), and use a model or method to combine all of that information into a summary format. Finally, the information needs to be presented in a format that can be quickly read and comprehended by the decision maker.

In some ways, the preparation of a PE report is more difficult than conducting original PE or outcomes research and preparing the results for publication. Not only does one need to consider multiple comparators for multiple disease states in multiple populations across multiple studies, but the results of all of these studies need to be summarized into a simple number or ratio to enable a recommendation to be made.

In the remainder of this chapter we'll explore the three essential elements of a PE report: assessing the validity and usefulness of PE studies, summarizing and modifying the results with data relevant to the user, and the format of the report itself. I'll then present a sample report that can be modified for use in your practice setting.

ASSESSING VALIDITY AND USEFULNESS

The first step in the preparation of the PE report is to conduct a complete literature search of PE and efficacy data concerning the use of the drug. Each article needs to be critically evaluated to determine if the methodology used was appropriate for objectives identified and if the conclusions reached are supported by the results of the study. For example, the author should have considered the use of techniques such as discounting and sensitivity analysis as appropriate. A more complete discussion of how to review clinical and PE literature can be found in Chapter 12 and Chapter 13, respectively.

After assessing the validity of studies (and discarding those studies whose design renders results invalid), the studies should be assessed for their usefulness. To do this, the following two questions must be addressed:

■ Do the studies use assumptions, measures of cost and efficacy, drugs, and a patient population similar or relevant to those at this site?

■ If the answer is no, is it possible to restate or recalculate the study results using data assumptions applicable to this site?

Studies that meet those criteria of validity and potential for usefulness may be used in the next step.

SUMMARIZING AND MODIFYING THE RESULTS

At this point, the preparer needs to use various methods of assimilating and summarizing the studies in order to make recommendations for formulary additions/deletions or inclusion in pathways. Generally, this will require some degree of restatement of the PE studies analyzed by including, at a minimum, the costs of health care resources consumed from the users' perspective. It may also involve using a PE model or technique in order to standardize or process the results of the different studies. However, a more detailed discussion of the techniques involved in this step is beyond the scope of this chapter.

A concern of both users and preparers of PE reports is whether or not the "most appropriate" PE methodology was selected in any one study or used in preparing the report itself. Personally, I'm more concerned about *adequacy of disclosure* of the methodology and assumptions rather than the identifica-

EXHIBIT 2

A sample of a pharmacoeconomic report prepared for presentation to the Formulary Committee

At your request, I have performed a pharmacoeconomic (PE) analysis of the currently available calcium channel blockers (CCBs) for the purpose of recommending which agents should be included on our hospital's formulary. The recommendations will be based on the criterion that only the most cost effective CCBs will be selected for formulary inclusion. The definition of PE and cost effectiveness and the necessary assumptions that I have made are described below.

Pharmacoeconomics is a tool (not a solution) used to determine which alternative is expected to be the most cost effective for a given patient population with a specific disease state. The alternative recommended is not necessarily the one with the lowest cost or the highest effectiveness; it's the one in which the average *desired level of effectiveness* can be achieved at the lowest possible cost. By application of different mathematical techniques and models, and combining cost and effectiveness measures into one ratio or number, selection of the alternative with the best "numerical rating" or "score" can be made. Alternatively, if a prescriber wants to use a drug that is more effective but has a lower cost-effectiveness "score," use of pharmacoeconimcs allows one to determine the incremental or marginal cost associated with the more effective drug. However, one must still decide if the extra cost is reasonable in light of the resources available, the need for a drug with higher efficacy, and the health care standards of the institution. (**introduction**)

The different drugs and dosage forms evaluated (and their acquisition prices to the hospital) may be found in Appendix I. For each disease state in which one of the CCB is used, I reviewed the primary and tertiary published literature regarding the relative effectiveness and associated toxicities of these CCBs. I also considered the recommendations of the hospital's cardiologists. As a private institution, we can use the formulary to shape drug selection choices; however, we need to also consider the likely home maintenance medication of the patients and the potential for therapeutic substitution of formulary agents for the patient's home medication. Therefore, I also considered the prescribing pattern of the hospital's attending physicians. (**sources of information**)

The perspective of my analysis was that of the hospital. This means I used the hospital's costs of drugs and treatment of the disease and drug toxicities as a basis for determining the costs and benefits associated with CCB therapy. Other perspectives, such as those of the physician, patient, or third party payer, might have resulted in different drugs being selected. (**perspective**)

I considered outcomes that might occur, and the applicable costs and benefits from this perspective by using PE studies that considered these measures over a 2-year period. (**time frame**)

Costs analyzed included all direct, tangible costs of treatment and toxicities that could vary or change with the use of these drugs. Omitted were costs that would be incurred by the patient, such as physician fees or out-patient therapy. I predicted future costs by combining the hospital's historic costs of treatment with the predicted patient census of the future. See Appendix II. (**definition of costs**)

Continued on next page

EXHIBIT 2 *(continued)*

Continued from previous page

The primary measure of effectiveness was coronary-event-free therapy. Secondary measures considered were incidences of toxicities and potential for drug interactions, number and type of FDA approved indications, number of available dosage forms, number of contraindicated disease states, differences in monitoring, expected patient compliance with the drug regimen, other disease states that could be treated concurrently, and suitability of this drug for the type of population at this hospital based on dosing adjustments that would be required because of impaired hepatic or renal function. See Appendix III. (**measure of effectiveness**)

The model used to determine the most cost-effective agent was cost-benefit analysis. All the benefits (i.e., reduction in coronary-related health care costs) of the alternative therapies are converted to dollars, and the drug(s) with the highest net benefits (benefits less therapy costs) were selected. See Appendix IV. (**model selected**)

I considered how the drugs would be used by the typical patient population in our institution—elderly patients with three to four concurrent disease states (at least one of which is cardiovascular in nature) and Medicare-insured patients, who typically use four to six other concurrent medications. (**population**)

CONCLUSION AND RECOMMENDATION

While CCB are referred to as a drug class, there are really three subgroups of CCB and I have addressed them separately. I believe there needs to be a representative from each class of agents due to their different effects on heart rate, cardiac output, and potential for interaction with other drugs.

I have also divided my recommendations between those agents that are on the formulary as "recommended" and those that should be included because of "convenience" or outside prescribing patterns.

Within the calcium channel blocker class, I recommend the following agents and dosage forms be included on the formulary:

1. Diltiazem. The least expensive once daily oral capsule among the current products plus a generic version of an immediate-release formulation.

2. Verapamil. Verelan, as the once daily formulation, plus a generic version of an immediate-release formulation.

3. Amlodipine (Norvasc), as the once-daily dihydropyridine.

I am also recommending that other commonly used agents be made available without permanent inclusion on the formulary until there has been an opportunity for physicians to alter their prescribing policy to the preferred formulary agents. Specifically, I recommend that a sustained-release version of nifedipine, an immediate-release version of nifedipine, and the drug felodipine (Plendil) be available to physicians for a 6-month transitional period, after which time their potential formulary status is evaluated. Consideration should also be given to automatic therapeutic substitution for nonformulary calcium channel blockers that may be ordered.

tion of the specific method and assumptions selected. (Refer to Exhibit 1 for further discussion of this topic.)

FORMAT OF USERS' REPORT

The last and perhaps most important step is to devise a format for presentation of your PE report that will maximize its usefulness and minimize confusion. To contrast with the PE report, a published PE study can be limited to a journal's article length requirements, is often designed to enable readers to replicate the model or techniques used, and is meant to be fully understandable on its own without explanatory comments. A PE report, on the other hand, can be designed differently since it is a hybrid of both analyses and recommendations. The analysis portion of the report can be as extensive as necessary, but details should be presented as appendices to the report itself. Often, decision makers rely on the verbal presentation and the PE report itself—rather than obtaining and reviewing the original PE studies upon which the report is based—to make their decision. The appendices provide further information that might be requested or needed.

As stated earlier, the report should be concise, yet complete. It should have the necessary degree of clarity and use technical expressions understood by readers with limited experience with PE (or contain sufficient definitions as necessary). Some common mistakes made by report preparers include:

- using PE terminology not familiar to the unsophisticated user,
- using irrelevant or unrequested perspectives (but that doesn't mean that more than one perspective is inappropriate),
- not defining terms that can be defined in more than one way, such as effectiveness, outcome, direct and indirect costs,
- failing to disclose the PE model or technique used when assembling the report,
- failing to use an important PE technique, such as sensitivity analysis, of the measures of cost and efficacy used in the report.
- trying to make the PE report resemble a publication, instead of a summary document (with assumptions and financial calculations attached as appendices).

The following is the 12-point outline I use when preparing a PE report. Of course, you may have other information you wish to include.

1. Begin with a brief introduction of what PE is and why it is being used to select from among alternative agents. Doing so might help overcome a suspicion voiced by others that I've encountered—that PE is simply a new ploy to use to recommend the use of the least expensive agent.

2. State the purpose of your report and the criteria used for making your recommendations. Don't use words such as "cost effectiveness" without explaining what it means.

3. State the drugs and dosage forms you've evaluated.

4. State the source of the information upon which your report is based—e.g., controlled studies or clinical trials, prospective or retrospective studies, actual patient data from the health system, or a literature based review.

5. State the perspective you chose for your report and define what that

means. If applicable, state that more than one perspective was considered and discuss the implications of using different perspectives.

6. State the time frame (over which costs were included and outcomes measured) used by you in your report. It may differ from that of some of the PE studies you reviewed.

7. Provide a definition of cost terminology. Define words such as "marginal or incremental costs," "fixed costs," "variable costs," and "opportunity costs," if used. You may also want to distinguish costs from patient charges.

8. Define the health care resources that were used in the studies examined. These cost components include such things as laboratory tests, personnel time, patients' length of stay, and other special procedures. State if toxicity costs or post-discharge follow-up costs were included in the studies.

9. State the primary and secondary outcome measures used to evaluate the effectiveness of therapy.

10. State and define the PE models or techniques used in the report and any important assumptions they were relied upon.

11. Define the patient population you anticipate to be the major user(s) of the drug(s).

12. State your conclusions and recommendations. Briefly provide the reasons why you recommend a certain agent. If sensitivity analysis was performed that might lead to a different conclusion, state that as well.

As an example, let me share with you an assignment I performed for an institution in conjunction with the evaluation of two new drugs of the dihydropyridine class. At that time, the formulary contained several different calcium channel blockers with different dosage forms, manufacturers, and dosing regimens. The goal of my assignment was to eliminate the "cost-ineffective" agents from the formulary and to recommend which of the calcium channel blockers (and the dosage forms) should be included for inpatient treatment of hypertension and angina.

In Exhibit 2, I've shown the format of the report I used when reporting the results to the P & T Committee. After reading the report, the P & T Committee accepted the recommendations and made the necessary formulary additions and deletions.

This chapter discussed the importance of the PE report as a means of communicating information to the end users of PE studies. remember that to meet the needs of decision makers, you not only need to perform a vlaid analysis of PE information but also need to communicate that information in an understandable and useful format.

Designing a complete, concise data collection form for outcomes research

Learning Objectives:

After reading this chapter, one should be able to:

1. List the five goals of data collection form design.

2. Describe the method of collecting and categorizing that is most suitable for each of nominal, ordinal, continuous, descriptive, and prevalence data.

3. Design a data collection form, for a retrospective chart review or observational study, which accomplishes the objectives of the study and meets the needs of the users.

Dear Dr. Basskin:

After reading one of your columns, we decided to take the plunge and start doing some outcomes research at our hospital. We followed all the planning steps you've suggested in Chapter 5 and conducted a pilot study in 10 patients. However, we aren't sure what to do with the data we've collected. Most of it is descriptive and seems to be different for every patient. Is there a better way of collecting and sorting this information to determine the average costs and efficacy for different drugs under consideration?

Dr. Zoe Harrison
Vancouver, BC, Canada

A s this reader has discovered, the usefulness of outcomes research is only as good as the quality of the data collected and one's ability to sort and analyze those data to reach conclusions. In this chapter, I'll discuss the considerations that go into designing a data collection form to ease the collection process and enable computerized sorting and analysis. The goals of data collection form design are to produce a form that

- is relevant to the research goals, and needs of the user,
- is easy to read and use,
- is complete yet concise,
- minimizes the risk of alternative interpretation of answers to questions, and
- facilitates easy data entry into a database for sorting and subsequent analysis.

To avoid collecting too much, too little, incorrect, or unusable data, I suggest the following step-by-step approach:

1. Identify the goal of the research and the summary/statistical information

EXHIBIT 1

Pitfalls to avoid in designing data collection forms

Among the problems in form design, which have been summarized in an excellent book by Spilker on performing clinical research, are the following:

1. Requesting information without providing adequate instructions on how to complete the form or interpret information.

2. Using multiple pages for a single category of information that could easily fit on one page.

3. Requesting more information than needed.

4. Including data subject to multiple interpretations.

5. Using unfamiliar jargon.

6. Failing to include all possibilities or an "other" category when using a check-off system to obtain responses.

7. Using too much descriptive data, which makes each answer to a question unique and difficult to combine or condense.

8. Using codes on the form relevant only to data processors or investigators, which makes the form difficult to complete by staff.

9. Not collecting sufficient data at baseline or after treatment.

10. Not collecting data at the relevant time period.

Adapted from Spilker B, *Guide to Clinical Trials.* New York: Raven Press, 1991:264 (chart 36.2).

needed by the user (e.g., to determine the cost effectiveness of each drug within a drug class or arm of a disease state management pathway).

2. Identify the patient population and perspective of the research.

3. Identify the measurable, relevant clinical, humanistic, or economic outcome(s) associated with the goals, determine how they will be measured, and determine when or how frequently the success/failure of achieving those outcomes will be measured.

4. Determine the pharmacoeconomic model to use to evaluate the cost and efficacy data.

5. Identify the extent of detail required by the user. Will you need to determine the cost of each drug or laboratory test used, or will the total cost of therapy be sufficient?

6. Determine the demographic or statistical information that's needed either for sorting data by demographic category or because it may independently affect outcomes or cost of therapy.

7. Identify the specific health care resources, such as drugs, laboratory tests, and ER admissions (not the costs or prevalence of each at this time), expected to be consumed or saved in the relevant time period under measurement.

8. Design a form to collect the information necessary to record and sort the data.

9. Collect the data and enter them in a computerized database.

10. Use the database's sorting and statistical capabilities to determine average cost, effectiveness, and cost effectiveness for different categories of patients (i.e., group the patients according to demographic or other characteristics).

SPECIFICS ON THE GOALS OF DATA COLLECTION DESIGN

Relevant to the goals of research and needs of the user. It is crucial that the data collection form be prepared after the research goals and outcomes to be followed are determined. Otherwise, one may be collecting data not relevant to the reason for the research. On occasion, the user may need the data sorted in a certain manner (e.g., by prescribing physician or patient age) or statistically analyzed in a certain way (e.g., by average length of stay or by total length of stay). Thus, these objectives also need to be considered when designing the form and deciding which data elements to collect.

Easy to read and use. The data collection form should be simple enough that the data collector does not need to constantly seek clarification from the form author. Also, if possible, the form should not contain questions that ask for information that is not readily available to the data collector. The order of the questions should also be logical—i.e., starting with the patient name and demographic data and progressing through to treatment and outcome of therapy. Finally, the form's layout should facilitate data entry. Each question should be structured to allow numerical or simple "yes/no" answers.

Complete yet concise data. Data collection should be based on one simple premise: there is a cost to collecting and analyzing data and a value of that information to the user. Therefore, the value of any additional information collected to aid the decision-making process should be greater than the cost of collecting it. Sometimes, when a retrospective chart review is performed, there is a tendency to collect everything about the patient while the chart is in the hands of the data collector. On the one hand, one certainly doesn't want to omit data that might be required for a subsequent analysis. This is particularly important when baseline data from a patient are needed, such as prior to the start of therapy or for a prospective study. On the other hand, all collected data will need to be entered into a database and eventually analyzed. The fewer the data points to enter, the more quickly data entry can be completed and analysis—uncluttered by unnecessary information—can begin.

Minimize alternative interpretations. Data that are subject to alternative interpretations or are judgment-based require special treatment. There needs to be a trade-off between the need for an accurate assessment and interpretation of laboratory tests and clinical symptoms versus consistency among data collectors. One solution is to have one person train all the data collectors. Another is to use only one data collector. Still another is to provide specific instructions for questions requiring the application of judgment. My preferred approach, and one I've demonstrated in the example this month, is to use a series of "yes/no" questions, so that a conclusion can be drawn based on attainment of a certain number of "yes" answers.

Facilitating data entry and analysis. There are two parts to consider in this section—the ways in which data are expressed or quantified and the method by which data are sorted, analyzed, and summarized.

To facilitate data entry and sorting, data need to be categorized in a quantitative manner. This is only possible if qualitative or descriptive data are converted into quantitative data. Let's try some examples of how this can be done.

The easiest type of data to work with are *nominal*, or "yes or no" data. The data sheet would contain a series of questions for which the only answer could be yes or no. For example, "Did the patient die?" and "Is the patient male?" are such questions. By formatting questions in this fashion one procures prevalence data—e.g., the percentage of patients who died or who are male.

Posing questions that require collection of **nominal data** is best reserved for cases in which there are only two possible answers. If there are more than two possible answers, a better approach is to list all possible answers and allow the one most suitable to be selected. For example, a question could ask, "Check off the drug selected from among the following choices: amoxicillin, penicillin, ampicillin."

This style of question also can be used to describe the reason for an event or choice of therapy. This approach also minimizes interpretation biases of data collectors—i.e., their need to explain or interpret different outcomes. When this technique is used, however, it's always important to allow for a "write-in" answer with room for an explanation, since one can never contemplate all the possible responses to such a question.

Data that can be entered as **continuous**, such as blood pressure or cholesterol levels, are also easy to record and sort. This type of data should be used whenever something is being measured and the answer can be given in discrete intervals.

Prevalence measurements (i.e., how many occurrences) work well when recording the quantity of health care resources used (such as length of stay, ER admissions, drugs administered).

Data that are difficult to work with involve responses requiring grading or ranking—e.g., severity of bleeding or extent of pain. Rather than try to describe each scenario in descriptive terms, consider allowing the use of a numerical ranking scale. These scales are subjective to some extent but do facilitate numerical sorting and analysis.

Data requiring achievement of long-term therapeutic goals can also be difficult to record in a quantifiable format. One alternative is to use quantifiable surrogate outcomes, such as serum cholesterol levels for progression of coronary artery disease, and hemoglobin A_{1c} levels for progression of diabetes complications. Another alternative is to use a checklist of diagnostic criteria, some or all of which must be met to categorize an outcome as having been achieved.

It is important to note that some data elements or circumstances are extremely difficult to measure or account for quantitatively. These include the precise reason for noncompliance, the existence of multifaceted outcomes,

EXHIBIT 2

Community-acquired pneumonia data collection form

Patient name _____ Date of admission _____

Age _____ Gender _____ Weight _____ Medical record number _____

Immunosuppressive concurrent therapy? yes/no
(Answer yes if currently undergoing chemotherapy or receiving oral steroids)

Comorbidity a factor? yes/no
(Answer yes if patient has diabetes, congestive heart failure, hepatic or renal failure, or is HIV positive)

Hepatic function satisfactory? yes/no
(Answer no if more than two of the following vary from normal values by at least 50%: AST, ALT, bilirubin, albumin)

Renal function satisfactory? yes/no
(Answer no if more than two of the following are true: Age > 65, serum creatinine >1.2 mg/100 ml, weight < 60 kg)

Prescribing physician _____

Drugs selected for empiric treatment	Route of adminis-tration	Number of doses given in first 48 hrs	Patient charge per dose	Dosed properly? (yes/low/high)
Erythromycin				
Clarithromycin				
Trimeth/sulfamethox				
Penicillin				
Cefazolin				
Ciprofloxacin				
Ceftriaxone				
Other				

Was the empiric therapy successful? yes/no
(Answer yes if afebrile, WBC is in normal range, and patient's other physical symptoms—such as cough or malaise—have improved)

If no, enter reason number_____
1) Clinical failure after 48 hours
2) Organism resistant per C & S
3) Physician chose to change antibiotics before 48 hours
4) Adverse drug event related to empiric antibiotic
5) Other _____

Organism revealed from culture and sensitivity
(or enter N/A if cultures were not taken or were negative) _____

Length of stay – ICU_____ **Length of stay (general med)**_____

Prepared by _____ **Date** _____

Data collection form used to assess the cost and success rates of alternative antibiotic regimens for the empiric treatment of community-acquired pneumonia.

Formulary/Source: L. Basskin, PharmD

the presence of multiple comorbidities, concurrent disease states, risk factors, concurrent drug therapies, the retrospective assessment of pain, and determination of quality of life. The optimal ways to address these issues continues to be studied and debated.

To enter and analyze data, statistics packages, such as SAS or SPSS, are available that have both database and statistical capabilities. However, these packages can be expensive and require a certain level of sophistication and expertise with statistics. My personal preference is to use a spreadsheet software program, such as Microsoft's Excel. These programs are easy to learn, relatively inexpensive, and often included in the purchase package of most computers. By using each column in the spreadsheet for a different data category, and each line for a new patient, large amounts of data can be entered. Other columns can be used to carry out simple calculations, such as combining prevalence of resource use with an average cost for that resource to determine total costs.

With these programs, it is very easy to sort and group data by different demographic or illness categories (though constantly recomputing the averages and totals for each group is somewhat labor intensive). Fortunately, built into these programs are complete statistical capabilities, which can be used by highlighting the data and running the statistics program.

EXAMPLE: A DATA COLLECTION FORM FOR PNEUMONIA

An example of a data collection form I designed to assess the costs and success rates of alternative antibiotic regimens for the empiric treatment of community-acquired pneumonia (CAP) is shown in Exhibit 2. The results of my study were to be used in the development of a critical care pathway for this illness. To this end, several issues needed to be considered. The administrators of our large community hospital were concerned about the potential widespread use of expensive, broad-spectrum antibiotics, which they suspected were being used unnecessarily. Length of stay fluctuated by several days for patients on different medications with apparently the same illness and risk factors. The decision regarding which drugs to include in the pathway would be based on a combination of a comprehensive literature search on the organisms and efficacy of antibiotics plus an actual review of our hospital's experience.

The goals of the research were to determine which of the antibiotics being used empirically for treatment of CAP in the hospital were the most cost effective (i.e., gave the best value for the money). Information on the choice of antibiotic following return of culture and sensitivity results were not collected, since the disease pathway was not going to address postempiric therapy.

I recommended conducting a retrospective chart review to identify "potential pathway" patients admitted with CAP within the previous 12 months. I made a list of specific questions to be answered (and data to be collected to answer them) before I could assess, and ultimately recommend, which antibiotics were most cost effective and should be considered for pathway inclusion. My questions were as follows:

1. Which of the antibiotics being used empirically were effective in curing

pneumonia in this hospital's patient population?

2. What are the typical organisms (and their level of resistance) associated with CAP in this community?

3. Was there a difference in effectiveness and/or cost of the different empiric drug therapies?

4. Did the extent of effectiveness or costs differ in patients of different ages or genders, or in the presence of comorbidities (e.g., hepatic or renal failure, diabetes, or immunosuppression)?

5. Did the length of stay and/or total cost of therapy differ between patients whose empiric therapy was successful versus those in whom it was unsuccessful?

Asking these questions enabled me to select the outcomes to track (causative organisms, length of stay, cost and effectiveness of different empiric antibiotics) and the health care resources used (empiric antibiotics, total cost of therapy). Without taking this step, I might have tried to collect too much individual information about use of other drugs, laboratory tests, and procedures before realizing that none of that information was needed in this case.

The time frame of the evaluation period was from hospital or emergency room admission to either return of culture and sensitivity results or 48 hours after therapy commenced, whichever was later. A positive outcome was defined as improvement in predefined criteria (temperature, white blood cell counts, other physical signs and symptoms; see Exhibit 2). A negative response was defined as the failure of empiric therapy, the need for a change to a different antibiotic (except a change from an intravenous antibiotic to an oral one after the above criteria have been met), or an adverse drug event requiring a change of antibiotics.

The perspective taken was that of a third-party payer, since this hospital, in the hope of capturing some of the managed care market, had set as its objective the reduction of patient charges. Accordingly, since the *total* charge was the concern, it was unnecessary to capture data regarding utilization of *individual* health care resources. An exception was made for length of stay, which I wanted to track in both the ICU and general medicine wards.

In selecting the patient population, I had to decide whether to exclude patients with all types of confounding variables (i.e., unique attributes that might result in therapeutic failures but are unrelated to the medications selected). I did not want to exclude patients with all of these problems because I wanted to know if some of these factors affected the success of empiric therapy. However, I did not want to include patients who might have acquired pneumonia from an atypical source. Therefore, I excluded patients living in nursing homes and those who had been recently admitted to the hospital. I also excluded patients admitted with concurrent "active" or acute exacerbations of disease, since one of these conditions might prolong the length of stay for reasons unrelated to pneumonia.

When I designed the data form, I assumed that I might not be the only data collector or person entering data into the database. To avoid different clinical interpretations of the same laboratory values, even if alternative interpretations were both possible and acceptable, I developed rules of interpretation. For example, instead of asking if hepatic function is satisfactory, I set the parameters by which liver function is to be assessed and asked the data collector to determine the answer to the question based on the results of these test parameters. In effect, I am forcing the data collector to replace his or her judgment with my own. This approach is particularly important to use when data are collected by students, residents, or others who may lack the experience or ability to make appropriate clinical interpretations without guidance. Note on the figure how the questions can all be answered either with numerical data (such as frequency or prevalence of use of a resource) or with a "yes/no" answers.

The drugs included on the form are the ones predominantly used in this institution as empiric therapy, based on a preliminary review of the charts. This approach is preferable to a "fill-in-the-blank" approach, since some data collectors may write in the trade names of drugs while others may write in the generic names, which can cause confusion for the data entry person. I also asked the data collector to calculate total doses, rather than the regimen ordered, since drugs ordered are not always administered. Finally, I wanted to know if the drugs were dosed in accordance with institution-specific guidelines to assess if improper dosing was a reason for a negative outcome.

After the data collection form was prepared, it was pilot-tested on a few charts and revisions were made. I used the revised form to collect information from the charts and was able to identify the following:

- the most common organisms associated with CAP in this institution;
- the most effective oral and intravenous antibiotics to use empirically;
- the extra length of stay in both the ICU and general medicine wards associated with unsuccessful empiric therapy;
- the unique patient factors that did and did not contribute to the success of empiric therapy;
- the physicians most often associated with selection of expensive or ineffective empiric therapy (not an original objective, but the information allowed us to develop a physician-specific education plan instead of a hospital-wide one); and
- a recommendation for the most cost-effective oral and intravenous antibiotics for inclusion on the critical care pathway.

In conclusion, the first step to constructing a well-designed data collection form is to identify the needed or desired research objectives and outcomes. Also, keep in mind that the form should be simple to complete, concise without omitting essential information that could be needed later, and suited to the collection of data that are easy to download and analyze via a computer software program.

Appendix I:
Solution to Chapter 12 practicum

The following are some of the major flaws in study design that limit this study's usefulness. How many of these flaws did you find?

1. The objectives of the study, while stated at the beginning, were disregarded when the methodology of the RCT was developed. The methods should have related directly to the objectives of selecting a benzodiazepine with a quick onset and long duration of action. Instead, patients were asked about the quality of their sleep.

Another potential flaw was that there was no mention that the questionnaire used to assess patients' quality of sleep was validated (i.e., does it evaluate what it purports to evaluate?). Without acknowledgment of validation one cannot even be sure that the answers to the questions correlate with the goal of the questionnaire, i.e., assessing the quality of sleep.

2. The starting dose in all patients was half the usual dose. Patients were allowed an additional half dose if requested, but there was no tracking of those who requested the extra dose. Consequently, we do not know whether the effective dose was the initial half-strength dose or the full-strength dose. The results of the RCT should have been stratified to let us know how many patients required the extra dose, and whether there was a difference in the results between those who took a half versus full dose.

3. The patients were not randomized between the groups; instead, admitting physicians were allowed to select the treatment group into which each patient was admitted. This admission bias could result in unequal patient characteristics in each group. For example, physicians might admit patients who had a particularly difficult time sleeping to a group with one of the comparator drugs, which was known to work. In this way, the group with Snorazapam may have had only patients for whom falling asleep was not truly problematic.

4. Patients were taking concurrent medications that might have affected the quality, onset, and duration of sleep. These "confounding variables" can directly affect the results. Ideally, patients with such confounding variables should have been excluded from the RCT. Alternatively, if the patients had been properly randomized between the three different treatment groups, it is (statistically) more likely that an equal number of patients with CNS stimulating drugs would have been assigned to each group.

5. No placebo control group was used. Some readers may agree with this decision on the basis of ethics (i.e., would it be fair to deprive a group of any of the drugs when there are proven remedies available?). Without a placebo control group, there is no guarantee that the results might not have been achievable without administering any drug. In fact, many hospitals have chosen to omit the general-use benzodiazepines for sleep (except in unusual cases) for precisely this reason.

6. No review of other concurrent medications or disease states was made.

Can the investigator rule out the possibility that the duration and quality of sleep might be attributable to factors other than the RCT medications?

7. The patients were not really blinded, since the identity of the drug was not concealed. It has been shown in studies that patients in an RCT who know they are assigned to the treatment group (versus the control group) tend to do better and report higher scores of satisfaction. This is probably due to a desire to "please" the investigators or to ensure they can stay in the program and receive free medicine or extra attention.

8. The investigator was not blinded. It is important for the investigator not to know the treatment group to which the subject belongs, particularly when one is administering subjective questions. The investigator should be neutral as to how the patients perform. This will avoid phrasing questions in different manners to patients of different groups or providing extra attention to a subject based on the group of "preference."

Despite the investigator's intent of remaining objective or indifferent to the results of the RCT, it is the rare investigator who has neither a preconceived idea nor a natural curiosity as to which of the treatment groups' results will be the most impressive. Accordingly, it becomes too easy to ask a subjective question or perform a measurement in a manner that favors one particular group.

9. There was neither an assessment nor a quantification made of the side effects attributable to each medication. While side effects were neither a primary nor secondary objective of this RCT, they represent important information for readers of the RCT. Not only could side effects result in admissions due to adverse drug events, prolonged admissions, and medical complications, they could reduce patients' compliance with their medication regimen. Unlike the results associated with highly compliant patients in an RCT, there is no guarantee that these "efficacy" results can be extrapolated to show effectiveness in "real" patients.

10. Patients who were not awake at drug administration time did not comply with the study protocol but were still administered questionnaires. These patients should have been excluded from the RCT.

My overall conclusion, after assessing this study, is that the design flaws are so significant that the cause-and-effect relationship cannot be shown to exist for Snorazapam.

Appendix II:
Primer on statistics

An understanding of commonly used statistical terminology is valuable when reading or performing a pharmacoeconomic analysis. This primer is meant to serve as an orientation or overview of some commonly used statistical terms. Readers who desire a more complete understanding of statistics and its applications are urged to consult a more detailed reference book.*

Statistical significance. An important use of statistics is to provide readers with some assurance that the results obtained are due to treatment effects and not sampling errors. The maximum sampling error rate generally accepted by the scientific community is 5% and is usually referred to as a p value of less than 0.05. This means that if the population were continually resampled, treated, and reevaluated, a difference in outcomes would be observed between those treated and those not treated in 19 out of 20 samples. In one sample out of 20, the observed difference would be due to sampling error and not to the treatment. The actual p value obtained in a study is a function of the average results or size of the difference discovered, the variance (see below), and the sample size. If a mathematical difference exists between the average results from two groups of patients (i.e., the treatment and control groups) for which the p value (maximum sampling error rate) is less than 5%, the difference is said to be *statistically significant*. A lower p value does not mean that the detected difference was greater or that it was more significant; it means that there is less likelihood that the results from treating the sample would not be representative of the results that would be obtained from treating the population. For example, a p value of 0.01 means there is a 1 in 100 chance that this sample was not representative of the population.

If the therapy also results in clinically different outcomes, the difference is said to be *clinically significant*. If the study simply uses the term "significant," one can't be sure of the type of significance to which the investigators are referring.

Range. In any sample, the actual results for any one participant may be very low (or even negative; i.e., the patient got worse, not better, with the drug) or very high. The difference between the lowest and the highest observation is called the *range*. When the range contains only one or two extreme or atypical cases (referred to as *outliers*), these outliers might be excluded from a subsequent analysis if the probability of their occurrence in the population is thought to be very low. On the other hand, if the extreme values included death, one might choose to look more closely at and compare the characteristics of these outliers with those of one's own patient population when conducting a subsequent study.

Mean, median. Instead of the range, the *sample mean* (mathematical av-

---

* Dawson-Saunders B, Trapp RG, eds. <u>Basic and Clinical Biostatistics</u> (2nd edition). Norwalk, CT: Appleton and Lange, 1994.

erage) or the *median* (middle value) is often used when performing further analysis of the results. The sample mean, however, is only an estimate of the population mean (the average results of treatment if the entire population were treated). While the average is a convenient way of reporting results, the number of people, or *frequency*, with which the average results (and results close to the average) occur also needs to be considered. As the frequency with which the average and scores close to it increases, there is more assurance that the mean from this sample is very close to the population mean.

Look at the graphs in figures 1 and 2 below. Each represents a distribution of changes in blood pressure after use of a different antihypertensive drug. The results, when plotted, have what is known as a *normal* or *bell-shaped distribution*. The assumption that the results for a population have a normal distribution requires the use of certain statistical measures over others. For example, the mean is the measure used for normal distributions (figures 1 and 2), while the median is the preferable measure for skewed distributions (figure not shown). Although figures 1 and 2 show the same mean change (20 mm Hg decrease), figure 1 has most of the values surrounding the mean while the values in figure 2 are widely distributed. Obviously, one should feel more assurance that the sample mean is a better estimate of the population mean for the drug depicted in figure 1 since there is a higher frequency and

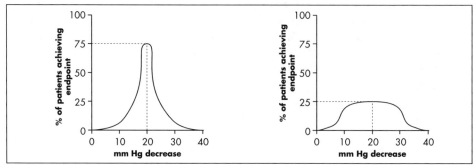

Figure 1   Figure 2

lower variance (see definition below) associated with that value. In figure 1, 75% of patients achieved the 20 mm Hg decrease in blood pressure, while only 25% in the comparative study arm (figure 2) achieved this degree of blood pressure lowering.

Variance, standard deviation, confidence interval. The extent to which all of the data obtained differ from the mean is called the *dispersion* and is measured by the *variance*, and from it such values as the *standard deviation* and *standard error of the mean* are calculated. The larger the variance, the more likely that distributions will resemble figure 2 compared with figure 1 and the more likely that either an individual result or the population mean could differ from the sample mean. Statisticians report not only the sample mean but also their estimate of the range in which the *real mean* of the population likely falls. This estimate of the range of the real mean is usually referred to as the *confidence interval* and is a mathematical calculation based on both the variance and the sample size. The interpretation (which is usually expressed at the 95% level) is that the researcher is 95% confident that the average results from treating the entire population with a drug would fall within this confidence interval. In other words, the mean obtained from one sample was just the average of that sample; the real expected results of the drug when administered to the population could fall anywhere within the confidence interval for that average. This is why it is important to consider the confidence interval and not just the sample mean when predicting the effect of the drugs studied in the relevant population.

Appendix III:
Predicting the future: Should modeling or patient-based outcomes research be used?

One of the reasons why pharmacoeconomic or outcomes research is conducted is to assist in predicting future developments in a patient population. One collects historical information about a given patient population and, after making reasonable assumptions about the future, attempts to predict the costs or outcomes associated with alternative disease states, therapies, or interventions. There are two general approaches that can be used to predict the future: modeling and patient-based outcomes research. The pros and cons of each as a practical, reasonable, and accurate method of predicting the future are described below.

Modeling. In modeling, the investigator usually uses or develops computer software and assumes that a definitive, quantifiable relationship exists between alternative therapies/interventions and probable clinical, economic, or humanistic outcomes. Instead of observing patients and collecting data over a defined time period, alternatives sources are used to represent the past or predict the future. Information about cost and efficacy may come from published clinical trials, expert panels, or governmental or institutional treatment costs reported elsewhere. The model also requires that assumptions be made about factors such as the extent to which the future costs and patients will be typical of the past. The usefulness and reliability of modeling as a predictive technique depend on three factors—the reasonableness of the assumptions used, the accuracy and appropriateness of the mathematical formula employed, and the use of sensitivity analysis to test the model's robustness (Do the model's conclusions hold true throughout the entire range of input values tested?).

There are two disadvantages associated with the use of modeling as a predictor of pharmacoeconomic outcomes. First, modeling generally is more susceptible to bias and manipulations than patient-based outcomes research is. Without "hard" data, you can include whatever costs and likelihood of outcomes you want to assume. Second, the "real published data" used in some models are often from controlled clinical trials conducted with narrow patient populations and in which drugs are administered or services are rendered under ideal conditions (as opposed to the types of patients likely to be subject to interventions in your institution). The best model is one that may use theoretical or efficacy data but allows you to insert your own data to see how the results would change.

Situations in which modeling would be preferred to patient-based outcomes research include the following:

■ actual patient data are insufficient, unreliable, inaccurate, irrelevant, incomplete, or inappropriate;

■ research using patients, costs, and outcomes typical of your own institution has already been conducted, published, and summarized using valid methodology;

■ measurement techniques for required individual patient data are unavailable, unsuitable, or unreliable, or they lack credibility or involve too much subjectivity in collection or interpretation;

■ too much time and too many resources would be required to obtain a statistically sufficient number of actual patients;

■ reasonable, reliable assumptions can be made about missing information or about the future;

■ either conclusions are required about large patient populations or it is not feasible to wait for patients with every combination of outcomes or confounding variables; and

■ the model, despite being based on assumed or non–institution-specific data, can be used in an institution-specific manner by allowing for easy substitution of real costs and real patient data.

Patient-based outcomes research. To conduct patient-based outcomes research, a statistically sufficient number of patients are followed before and after an intervention, and the extent to which a designated outcome is achieved is measured. Information about the cost of therapies/interventions is determined from actual measurement of the costs of care for each patient.

Compared with modeling, patient-based outcomes research has the advantage that it uses real patient outcomes data and real institutional costs and thus is likely to be a better predictor of costs, outcomes, and cost effectiveness in your own setting. The disadvantage is the time and manpower required to perform such research, as well as the need to locate and evaluate an adequate number of patients.

The method selected is generally a function of the availability and reliability of individual patient data and the quality of assumptions that have to be made. I recommend pure modeling when it is not possible to accumulate sufficient and reliable cost and outcomes data about a designated patient population, when there are cost or time limitations, or when adequate and credible measurement techniques do not exist or cannot be employed at a reasonable cost. Otherwise, I prefer patient-based outcomes research, as it is more institution- and population-specific. For the latter approach, I still recommend developing a mathematical model (using spreadsheet software), as it allows for easy determination of the relationship between costs and outcomes and allows for both sensitivity analysis and consideration of "what if" scenarios. Of course, approaches that employ a combination of both methods are also extremely useful.

Index

Notes

Notes